KOKOLOGY

The Game of Self-Discovery

Tadahiko Nagao and Isamu Saito

BARNES
&NOBLE
BOOKS
NEW YORK

This is a one-volume edition of *Kokology* and *Kokology 2,* published individually by Fireside, an imprint of Simon & Schuster, Inc.

Kokology:
Originally published in Japan by Seishun Publishing Co., Ltd., 1–12 Wakamatsu-cho, Shinjuku-ku, Tokyo as SOREIKE KOKOLOGY © 1998
Compilation and English translation copyright © 2000 by I. V. S. Television Co., Ltd., and Yomiuri Telecasting Corporation

Kokology 2:
Originally published in Japan by Seishun Publishing Co., Ltd., 1–12 Wakamatsu-cho, Shinjuku-ku, Tokyo as SOREIKE KOKOLOGY © 1998
Compilation and English translation copyright © 2001 by I. V. S. Television Co., Ltd., and Yomiuri Telecasting Corporation

This edition specially printed for Barnes & Noble Books by Simon & Schuster, Inc.

2003 Barnes & Noble Books

ISBN 0-7607-4083-6

Printed and bound in the United States of America

03 04 05 06 07 08 MC 9 8 7 6 5 4 3 2

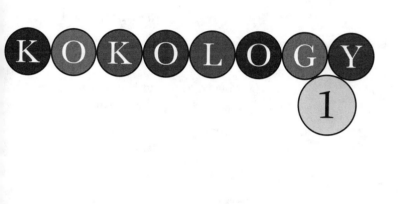

THE KOKOLOGY PROJECT TEAM

WRITERS	Tadahiko Nagao and Isamu Saito
EXECUTIVE PRODUCER	Hisataka Saito
GENERAL PRODUCER	Tadahiko Nagao Takanori Ikeda
TEAM STAFF	Shinichi Iwata Daisuke Shidara
COOPERATOR	Keiko Higashiomori
ILLUSTRATOR	Makoto Ishizuki
TRANSLATOR	Douglas Sipp, Office Miyazaki, Inc.
SPECIAL THANKS TO	James C. Vines Seiichiro Shimono Hisako Ishizuki Toshihide Ochiai Takeshi Itoh
SUPERVISOR	Isamu Saito

CONTENTS

CONTENTS

KOKOLOGY 101

kokology \ kō kōl´ ō jē \ *n* [Japanese, *kokoro*, mind, spirit, feelings + Greek, *-logia*, the study of] **1.** A series of psychological games designed to uncover emotional and behavioral traits of the players **2.** A popular term for the interpretation of the hidden meanings of human behavior and situational responses — **kokologist** *n* — **kokological** *adj* — **kokologize** *vi*

A WORD FROM PROFESSOR SAITO

T he eyes of the mind peer in two directions. One faces the outside world, gathering information about the environment and the people around us. The other is turned inward and looks at the hidden world of the inner self. This is the eye you use to survey the workings of your own mind, to ponder what others might be thinking, and to gaze into the future and foresee the kind of person you may one day become.

Many forms of media, such as books, newspapers, and television, have been developed to help people learn about and understand the outside world. It could be said that the media explosion of recent years has created a state of sensory and information overload, where every day we are faced with more data than we can possibly assimilate. But there are far fewer media to help us explore and understand the world within. Psychological games are one such medium, designed to help open the inner eye and sharpen its sight. The science of psychology itself allows people to study and comprehend the mind, but like any science, it demands time, hard work, and dedication to learn and uses a specialized vocabulary that keeps many nonspecialists at a distance. Kokology is a game based on the science of psychology, but with a fun and easy approach that makes it possible for everyone to experience and enjoy the world of the mind.

Kokology also works as a communications tool. For many people, the words *psychological test* evoke a dark or frightening image.

I'm a psychologist myself, and even *I* don't like to take them. But psychological games make the same process of discovery interesting and fun, and people feel less threatened when they view the experience as just a form of play. In Kokology it's okay to disagree with the interpretation of a quiz answer if it sounds crazy or unbelievable—that's part of the fun. But I think you'll find more often than not that you're surprised at how accurately the answers reflect people's true personalities, including your own. This makes the game a great way to bridge communication gaps between friends and lovers, to bring you closer together and help you understand each other better, to open up conversations on what might otherwise be difficult, sensitive, or forbidden subjects.

I have tried to make Kokology as entertaining as possible, while keeping true to the principles of psychological science. I hope you enjoy the time you spend playing and that you feel you've learned something about yourself and others in your life when you're done.

Isamu Saito
Professor, Rissho University

PLAYING THE GAME

W hen we set out to develop Kokology, our first and foremost goal was to make it fun. After all, who in their right mind would want to play a game that isn't? The basic concept was already there—our plan was to create a game where people would imagine themselves in everyday situations and unusual scenarios and respond to simple questions. The answers are interpreted from a psychological perspective and tell us something about the way that person's mind works. It's kind of like a Rorschach test that uses words instead of inkblots.

The concept was the easy part. The hard part was keeping the balance between science and fun. Professor Saito can vouch for the science; only you can be the judge of whether we've succeeded on the fun side. I'm not a psychologist myself, but I do understand enough about human nature to know that people don't like long introductions—especially not to a book of games. So I'm going to end by leaving you with a list of eight tips for making your experience with Kokology satisfying, enlightening, and fun.

Enjoy!

—TADAHIKO NAGAO

Eight Tips for Playing Kokology

1. Say the first thing that pops into your head.
The games work best when you don't hesitate or agonize over your choice of words. There are no right or wrong answers, so just relax and say whatever springs to mind.

2. Play with other people if you can.
Kokology can be read alone like any other book, but it's most enjoyable, exciting, and entertaining when you play with a partner or in a group. It's a chance to have a few laughs and get to know each other better. You may find that you have more in common than you ever suspected. On the other hand, you may find you're so incompatible that it's as though you're from different planets. There's only one way to find out for sure.

3. Don't try to predict the answers.
It's natural to want to try to outsmart the quizzes or guess what their hidden meanings may be. But what are you going to learn from that?

4. Be honest with yourself.
Kokology may be only a game, but like any good game, it can teach you something about yourself if you let it. Don't be afraid to accept the truth when a minor fault or shortcoming of yours is exposed. I can sense that you're basically a good, intelligent, and likable person. You bought this book, didn't you?

5. Be prepared.

Some of the quizzes will ask you to write something down or draw a picture, so it's a good idea to have a pen or pencil and some paper handy before you start. Advanced-level Kokologists might want to try videotaping a round of games at the next office party. The expressions on people's faces when their true characters are revealed can be priceless. And the secrets they unwittingly blurt out might be worth good money, too.

6. Don't read ahead.

This goes along with the advice of not trying to guess the answers, but it's directed at the group that likes to read the last page of a mystery novel first. Why not open yourself up to a few surprises? Is it really so satisfying to be able to say, "Oh, I knew it all along"?

7. Watch people's reactions (including your own).

The interpretations to the scenarios given in this book are only a starting point for learning more about yourself and others. Sometimes it's more instructive (and entertaining) to see how someone reacts to an answer that's a bit off target than it is to read an interpretation that's right on the money.

8. Keep an open mind.

In Kokology, as in life, it's important to keep things in perspective. There are no correct answers and more than one way of reading any situation. If you're playing with friends, take the opportunity to learn from and about them. What fun would the world be if we all thought alike? Variety is the spice of life.

1

A Desert Journey

Your desktop is spilling over with unfinished paperwork; the rest of the office has already gone home for the night. You look up at the clock and it laughs back. You wonder, with a sinking feeling inside, if this job will ever be done.

The professor drones on and on through a three-hour double lecture on the world's most boring subject. There's no space left for doodles in your notebook, and you're only thirty minutes into the class. You begin to think you've somehow been frozen in time.

Waiting can be a special form of torture, worse than any momentary pain. The combination of frustration and boredom can send even the bravest heart into a state of panic. Our first journey will bring us face-to-face with the infinite. Take a moment to prepare yourself, and enter the eternal desert. . . .

1. You are riding a camel across the vast and empty expanse of a seemingly endless desert. You have ridden until you are near exhaustion. What words would you say to the camel that has carried you all the way?

2. Just at the point when you thought you'd die of thirst, a beautiful oasis appears. But someone has arrived before you. Who is this other traveler? (Use the name of a person you know.)

3. Time passes slowly in the desert, and it feels like an eternity before the lights of a town appear on the horizon. You have finally reached your destination. What are your feelings as you come to your journey's end?

4. The time has come to part with the camel you have ridden for so long. Just as you dismount, a new rider climbs into the saddle to take your place. Who is the new rider? (Name another person in your life.)

KEY TO A DESERT JOURNEY

$\left(T\right)$ he desert and camel theme symbolizes the journey toward personal independence. Specifically, this scenario reveals your feelings about parting with a lover. Your answers show how you might react when the time comes to go your separate ways.

1. The words you spoke to the camel reveal what you might say to yourself when you realize love has been lost. Did you try words of encouragement like "We'll make it through somehow!" or "Don't worry, this can't go on forever"? Or was there a hint of despair— "We're lost . . . this is hopeless . . . I think we're going to die out here"?

2. In psychological terms, the oasis symbolizes the key to solving one's problems. The person you encountered here could be someone who has helped or comforted you in the past or one you might turn to in times of need.

3. The town at journey's end stands for the order restored to your emotions once you've recovered from your broken heart. Your feelings upon reaching the town are your true feelings about finally getting over a lost love.

4. The new rider is a person toward whom you feel a secret rivalry, jealousy, or resentment. Is the person you named a rival in love or maybe someone who once broke your heart?

THE BLUE BIRD

O ne day a blue bird suddenly flies through a window into your room and is trapped. Something about this lost bird attracts you, and you decide to keep it. But to your surprise, the next day the bird has changed color from blue to yellow! This very special bird changes color again overnight—on the morning of the third day it is bright red, and on the fourth it turns completely black. What color is the bird when you wake up on the fifth day?

1. The bird doesn't change color; it stays black.
2. The bird turns back to its original blue.
3. The bird turns white.
4. The bird turns golden colored.

KEY TO THE BLUE BIRD

(T) he bird that flew into your room seemed like a symbol of good fortune, but suddenly it changed color, making you worry that happiness would not last. Your reaction to this situation shows how you respond to difficulties and uncertainty in real life.

1. Those who said the bird stays black have a pessimistic outlook.

Do you tend to believe that once a situation goes bad, it never really returns to normal? Maybe you need to try thinking, If this is as bad as it gets, it can't get any worse. Remember, there's no rain that doesn't end and no night so dark that there's no dawn the next day.

2. Those who said the bird turns blue again are practical optimists.

You believe that life is a mix of good and bad and that it doesn't pay to fight against that reality. You accept adversity calmly and let things run their course without undue stress or worry. This outlook lets you ride out the waves of adversity without being swept away.

3. Those who said the bird turns white are cool and decisive under pressure.

You don't waste time on fretting and indecision, even when a crisis develops. If a situation gets too bad, you feel it's better to cut your losses and look for another route to your goal rather than getting bogged down in needless grief. This proactive approach means that things seem to just naturally go your way.

4. Those who said the bird turns golden can be described as fearless.

You don't know the meaning of pressure. To you, every crisis is an opportunity. You might be compared with Napoleon, who said, ". . . impossible: the word is not French." But be careful not to let your boundless confidence get the best of you. It's a very fine line between fearless and foolhardy.

A Night at the Symphony

There's something magical about a night at the symphony—a sense of expectation and pure pleasure. Imagine being able to take a place on that stage among the other musicians, a once-in-a-lifetime chance to perform at your very best.

If you could join the orchestra, what instrument do you see yourself playing?

1. Violin
2. String bass
3. Trumpet
4. Flute

KEY TO A NIGHT AT THE SYMPHONY

(M) usical instruments are symbolic of members of the opposite sex. The pairing of you and your instrument shows how you perceive yourself in making the music of love. The instrument you chose gives insight into what you think of as your strongest lovemaking technique.

1. Violin

The violin demands sensitive fingerwork and a delicate touch with the bow to draw forth music from the taut strings. You see yourself as having the same awareness and skill in locating and playing upon your partners' most sensitive points. There's a sense of adventure in the way your hands can create such beautiful music by running over the same familiar notes.

2. String bass

There's a feeling of power gotten from taking position behind an enormous bass and making it call out in a tremendous moan. In love, your skill rests in the ability to bend your partners to your will, taking complete control, and driving them onward to pleasures they never imagined they could experience. You never ask permission, but that dominating character is what makes you so irresistible.

3. Trumpet

There's no getting around it—your mouth is the strongest weapon in your arsenal. Whether it's whispering love talk in your partner's ear or exploring them with your lips, you have all the characteristics of the oral personality.

4. Flute

The flute demands incredible patience from those who want to master it. You show that same patience in the way you wear down partners with your persistence, determination, and stamina. Your lovers are often taken off guard when what they thought would be a brief recital quickly develops into a full concerto in six movements.

ON YOUR BIRTHDAY . . .

Your birthday is the one day a year when you're justified in expecting things to be just a little nicer than usual. Well wishes and congratulations, presents and cards, maybe even a party or a romantic dinner for two.

It's your birthday today, and when you check your mailbox you see you've gotten a card from someone you would have never suspected. Who is the sender? You have also received a number of gifts from family and friends. Of that group, who sent you the biggest package? (Give the names of people in your life when answering this quiz.)

KEY TO ON YOUR BIRTHDAY . . .

(T) he responses you gave signify your true feelings about people in your life, feelings you might not even be aware of yourself.

The person who unexpectedly sent you a card is actually someone you would like to care more about you or give you more attention. In short, the person you named as the sender is someone you worship from afar. Is it someone you barely know, someone you've been hesitant to approach, or just a friend you haven't heard from in a while? Maybe it's time you made the first move toward bridging that gap.

On the surface, you might associate the biggest package you received with good feelings about the sender. But from a psychological perspective, the person you named as the sender is actually someone whose affections you take for granted. This doesn't necessarily signify a lack of respect, but you definitely feel confident of their feelings for you. Be careful not to get overconfident. What feels like security to you may look like plain selfishness to others.

PICTURES AT AN EXHIBITION

Every once in a while it's nice to take a break from your busy schedule and experience the world of art firsthand. Some of us go to concerts or plays, some take up dance or a musical instrument, others try their hand at crafts. And of course there's always a trip to a museum. . . .

You are standing in front of a painting at an art museum, hands clasped behind your back as you try to take it in, when a total stranger comes up alongside you and says something to you. Which of the following does the stranger say?

1. "Isn't that a beautiful picture?"
2. "What do you think of this painting?"
3. "Excuse me, do you have the time?"
4. "You know, I happen to be a painter myself."

KEY TO PICTURES AT AN EXHIBITION

W) hen a stranger suddenly speaks to you there's always a
momentary mix of apprehension and expectancy. In this
imaginary scenario, the words the stranger spoke actually reflect
how you react in chance encounters and when meeting others.
Your answer reveals what kind of impression you make when meeting someone for the first time.

1. "Isn't that a beautiful picture?"

Your friendly and positive nature creates a great first impression on almost everyone you meet. Your only concern should be
that people may not take you seriously at first.

2. "What do you think of this painting?"

You're the type who likes to feel out the other person's tem-
perament before committing yourself to anything. People can sense
that hesitancy, and it may color their reactions to you. You won't
step on any toes with your cautious approach, but you may end up
living on other people's terms.

3. "Excuse me, do you have the time?"

To half the world you seem like an all right sort, but to the
other half you look just a little strange. You create a first impression of living life at your own pace and maintaining an individu-
ality that some would call eccentric. You don't place much

importance on what others may be thinking or feeling. For better or worse, therein lies the secret to you.

4. "You know, I happen to be a painter myself."

On first meeting someone, you come across as a little bit nervous and overeager. Maybe you're just trying too hard to be liked, but the harder you try, the worse an impression you make. Don't worry so much about making people think you're great—they'll like you better if you just loosen up and relax.

DEEP IN THE MOUNTAINS

The mountains and the sea—nature has a power that draws us to her. After all, we are all nature's children, born into her world and fed on her bounty. No matter what marvels technology may develop, getting back to nature lets us feel truly alive. Medical science may make advances, but the best medicine will always be nature's own healing power.

Your next journey will take you back to that green world, and what better setting for you to rediscover your natural self?

1. You have set off to climb a mountain, in search of a fabulously rare stone. What is your impression of the mountain as you stand at its foot?

2. After a hard search, you still haven't found the stone, and now the sun has fallen. What will you do next?

3. You have finally discovered the stone you were seeking. What kind of stone is it? Describe its size, weight, and value.

4. Now it is time to come down from the mountain and return home. What parting words do you have for the mountain, and what is its reply?

KEY TO DEEP IN THE MOUNTAINS

(T) he mountain that looms before you represents your father, or a father figure in your life. In psychological terms, it is a manifestation of the archetype of the "wise old man." The stone you seek symbolizes abilities and strengths you must discover within yourself on your own journey to adult independence.

1. Your impression of the mountain shows the image you have of your father. Was it difficult and unforgiving? Gentle and easily conquered? Or did you have an idealized image of a magnificent peak that somehow seemed to welcome you and encourage you in your quest?

2. The stone you are searching for represents your as yet undiscovered talent or strength. Your response to this question shows whether you will ever realize that untapped potential.

People who say they'd keep searching for the stone no matter what tend to show the same persistence and determination in their own lives, never giving up even when efforts seem fruitless.

Those who said they'd call it quits for the day but come back again to continue the search are the type who pace themselves, spreading their efforts over a long period of time. There are probably more than a few late bloomers in this group.

People who gave up looking for the stone altogether are in danger of never fulfilling their true potential.

3. The way you described the stone shows your feeling of self-worth. How big and heavy was it, and what did you think of its value?

"Oh, about twenty dollars or so," Hmmm, that's not much of an appraisal, is it?

"It turned out to be a huge diamond worth millions!" Hold on now, let's not get carried away with ourselves.

4. Your parting words to the mountain reveal what you have always wanted, but never been able, to say to your father. The mountain's reply shows your idea about his feelings for you. Do you recognize any of these patterns?

You: "Thanks for everything."

Mountain: "You take care of yourself."

Did you have that kind of ideal exchange? Or did it go more like this:

You: "Well, it looks like I'm finally through with you."

Mountain: "You can say that again!"

Maybe it's time you and your father sat down for a talk.

THE FORGOTTEN WALLET

It's a morning like any other: last-minute preparations before you run out the door. Hair? Check. Clothes? Check. Everything's ready to go. . . .

You get on your way at the usual time, but halfway to work you realize your wallet is not where you always keep it. A quick search confirms the worst—you left it at home! And there's no time for you to turn around and go back for it. You begin going through your pockets and bags to see how much spare cash you have to get you through the day. How much money do you find?

KEY TO THE FORGOTTEN WALLET

(T) he amount of cash you found represents the amount of money you forget about in your daily life; money you don't rely on being there. It also represents the amount of money you feel comfortable lending to others. Just how much did you say you found?

About ten or twenty dollars? That seems like a reasonable figure.

More than a hundred? You're probably popular with friends just before payday.

Nothing at all? Maybe you're broke, or are you just cheap?

BLUE COAT, YELLOW COAT

G athering in the town square for the lighting of the Christmas tree gives people a chance to come together as a community and celebrate the end of another year. It's a time of nostalgia and a chance for new memories to be born. People are in the holiday spirit, strangers act like friends, and a sense of peace is all around.

The night is cold, and you have come with a group of friends and acquaintances to watch the lighting of the tree. In the group of people with you, one person is wearing a yellow coat and another person is in blue. Who are the people wearing the blue and yellow coats? (Give the names of people you know.)

KEY TO BLUE COAT, YELLOW COAT

I n psychology, bright colors such as yellow are associated with warm and positive feelings, while cool colors like blue are linked with cold, negative emotions. It may surprise even you, but the person you named as wearing the yellow coat is someone you like or who makes you feel happy, while something about the person in the blue coat leaves you cold.

WRITTEN IN THE STARS

When you look up into a star-filled sky at night, sometimes it's possible to lose yourself in the infinite depths of space. We may be aware of their vast distances from earth, yet the stars still look like friendly messengers and granters of dreams when we see them twinkling in the dark. As the hours grow late, it's a comfort to look up and have their distant power to draw upon.

For this next game, you'll need paper and a pencil.

1. First, draw three stars of different sizes.
2. Next, draw a comet's tail on one (and only one) of your stars.

KEY TO WRITTEN IN THE STARS

T he stars combine a glittering image of the power to grant wishes and make dreams come true with a sense of distance and unattainability. Stars determine our present and give a hint of things to come. Your drawing illuminates your work life in general and your current career path in particular.

1. The largest star you drew represents the job you hold now, its potential and its disappointments. If the difference in size between that star and the other two is not very great, it signifies dissatisfaction or at least disinterest in your career, a willingness to shop around and keep your options open. Watch for an unexpected call from a headhunter. They have ways of finding these things out.

On the other hand, if your job star is much larger than the others, it indicates you're deeply absorbed and committed to your current path. Your concern should be not to fall into the trap of workaholism. All work and no play is no way to live.

2. In cultures throughout history and around the world, comets have been seen as harbingers of disaster and cataclysmic change. The star you gave a comet's tail to represents trouble looming on the horizon. If it's on one of the smaller stars, you're in luck; the heavens have overlooked you for now. But if your largest star is a comet, it might be a good time for you to bring your résumé up-to-date. The stars never lie.

SWEET MEMORIES

What is it about reminiscences of childhood that stir the heart so deeply and make us long to turn back the clock? Is it that sense of returning to innocence or just the pleasure of feeling young again? Those were the days when every toy, doll, and game was a special kind of treasure. The collector's mania for antiques and memorabilia has its roots in these childhood fascinations and the desire to relive the past, if only for a short while.

Our next encounter will take us back to that simpler time, to a little candy shop down the street. Perhaps you'll find your younger self among the goods in stock.

1. Inside the candy store, you find rows and rows of the old familiar candies, chocolate bars, chewing gums, and sweets from your youth. Some are stacked in organized shelves, some are loose in baskets and jars. What candy do you pick first, and why did you choose it? (Give the full reason behind your choice.)

2. While you're wandering the store making selections, you notice that outside a group of children look as though they're getting ready to enter the store. How many children actually come in?

3. You make your purchases and go home with a bag of candy. But when you open the bag, you see that the shopkeeper has added

some free extra candies as a special treat for you. How many extras did you get?

4. You've been thinking about giving the candy you bought as a gift to someone. To whom, if anyone, would you give it?

KEY TO SWEET MEMORIES

$\left(T\right)$ he candy theme harkens back to the time in your life when you could count on an occasional treat and even expect to be spoiled. This scenario reveals your expectations of others and your level of dependence.

1. What did you choose first from the almost endless selection? More important, why did you choose it? The reasoning behind your choice actually shows what you desire most from other people.

If you thought something like "I'd take the one with the secret toy surprise in the pack" you're likely the type who responds well to people bearing gifts. (And, turning that around, you might not be so positive toward those who turn up empty-handed.) Beware of becoming too materialistic. There's more to life than trading cards, iron-ons, and secret decoder rings.

If you said you chose the candy because you remember how good it tasted or it made you feel nostalgic, you are hungry for the same attention and affection you received from your mother as a child. Men, if you answered this way, you may be looked on as something of a mama's boy.

If you made your decision based on external factors like "I liked the wrapper" or "It looked cool," you're the type of person who makes judgments based on appearance alone. Just remember, it's the candy you eat, not the wrapper.

2. The number of children who entered the store while you shopped represents the number of people in your life you need to depend on. We all need support, whether it's actual physical assistance in the work we do or just encouragement from the people we love. You can't go through life completely on your own. But it's also true that relying too much on others makes it difficult to achieve personal autonomy.

Most people imagine between one and five children entering the store. People who said more than five children came into the store still have a way to go before they reach an adult level of independence. But those who said no children come in also might need to reconsider the way they look at the world.

3. The number of free treats you got reveals how much you still depend on your mother. The amount of special attention the storekeeper showed you is a measure of the attention you actually want from your mother. Most adults say one or two pieces. If you answered ten or twenty, you may need to think about spreading your wings a little more and flying away from the nest.

4. To whom would you give the candy? The person you chose is a person you would like to be able to take care of someday or have become dependent on you. Did you say you gave it to your parents? Your wish may be a reality sooner than you think.

Was it your partner or a person you secretly like? It might be fun taking care of them for a day or two, but that could wear thin.

Or did you say you wouldn't give the candy to anyone? You prefer a life with few attachments, asking little from the world and expecting the same in return. That solitary approach means you may never have to share with anyone, but it also means you may never have anyone to share with.

THE RIDE OF YOUR LIFE

Even for people with normally happy lives, there come times when the everyday seems just a little boring and, well, everyday. Although it's certainly nice to be able to know that tomorrow will be a good day, too much predictability can leave you uninspired. But we know a way to escape that daily routine, if only for a short while. The answer lies in seeking out stimulation and the occasional thrill. This is the secret to being able to appreciate the value of even our everyday lives.

How do we bring thrills into our lives? Watching movies, traveling, and playing sports and games of chance. Or maybe a trip to an amusement park, a world where thrills mingle with fantasies. Let's take a trip back to that realm of childhood excitement and fun.

You will need a pencil and paper for this quiz.

1. You enter the park gate, and a roller coaster looms before you with a line of people waiting their turn. How long do you have to wait in line before getting to ride?

2. Your turn finally comes and now you're racing and plunging around the course. What kinds of feelings does the speed bring out in you?

3. At the most exciting point in the course, the roller coaster dives into a pool of water and you're drenched by the spray. What do you shout or scream at this instant?

4. Next you decide to try the merry-go-round. But during your ride, for some reason the horse you're riding breaks down and stops moving. What do you say to the horse?

5. Your ride on the roller coaster was exciting, but it wasn't all that it could have been. If you were going to design the perfect roller coaster, what would the course look like? Draw a detailed picture of the course.

KEY TO THE RIDE OF YOUR LIFE

(D)id you have a good time in the park? In psychological terms, rhythmical up-and-down motions represent sexual excitement. So your responses to the five questions actually show your attitudes toward sex.

1. The time you spent waiting in line reveals how much time you spend, or would like your partner to spend, on foreplay.

Did you have to stand in line for hours before the main event, or did you just jump aboard without waiting?

2. Your feelings during the roller-coaster ride reveal how you feel while making love.

Did you think, "This is the best ride I've ever been on!" or was your reaction closer to, "Get me off this thing! I think I'm gonna throw up!"

3. In Jungian symbolism, water represents the source of life. Your words at the moment the roller coaster splashed into the pool show what you might say at the moment of sexual climax.

Let's hope you didn't say anything you'll end up regretting in the morning.

4. The horse, in psychosexual terms, is a symbol of the masculine principle. Your words to your broken-down steed reflect what you might say to yourself or to your partner in situations where the man failed to rise to the occasion.

"It's all right, don't worry about it. It's only a ride." You have a truly gentle and forgiving nature.

"I can't believe this. I want my money back!" You said it, not me.

"Come on you stupid animal, giddyap!" Yikes!

5. Your plan for the ideal roller-coaster course shows your vision of the perfect sex life.

The ups and downs of a roller-coaster ride are an exact metaphor for the thrills and lulls of lovemaking. Was it a long, slow ascent followed by a terrifying plunge? A series of acrobatic loop-the-loops and 360-degree rolls? Or maybe you drew a course where you spend the whole ride turned upsidedown and backward? Don't worry, your secret is safe with us.

YOU'RE ONLY HUMAN

I can't believe it! How could I do something so stupid?" We have all too many chances to say those words. Burned toast, coffee stains on paperwork, sleeping through the alarm clock, stubbed toes, missed exits—it's human nature to goof up once in a while. Nobody's perfect, and each of us proves that every day. Keep that in mind the next time you're tempted to laugh at other people's careless mistakes. After all, you never know when it'll be your turn to wear mismatched socks to work.

You're walking down the street, thinking of other things, when you stumble into a garbage can on the sidewalk and knock it over. What comes spilling out from under the lid?

1. Nothing comes out—the can was empty.
2. A pile of loose trash spills out onto the street.
3. Apple cores, chicken bones, and other raw garbage.
4. A well-tied black plastic garbage bag.

KEY TO YOU'RE ONLY HUMAN

I n your carelessness you overturned a garbage can, dumping out something that had been neatly shut away and exposing it for all the world to see. Your image of the can's contents reveals things inside you that you try to hide from public view.

1. Nothing comes out—the can was empty.

People who gave this answer tend to live their lives without making displays or false pretenses. What you see is what you get. It's this simple honesty that gives them their charm.

2. A pile of loose trash spills out onto the street.

Those of you who said the can was full of loose trash may seem to be straightforward and forthright to others but actually have a pile of unexpressed feelings locked up within. You may notice these feelings only as a general sense of frustration, but when you think about it, aren't there places where you've been holding back from saying the things you really feel?

3. Apple cores, chicken bones, and other raw garbage.

People who imagined a pile of kitchen waste are suppressing their appetites and the natural desire for food. Maybe you're on (or just avoiding) a diet. Or trying to save money by cutting back on eating expenses. Whatever the case, it's taking its toll on you.

There's no need to overdo it, but it might do you good to spend a well-earned night out at a restaurant with friends.

4. A well-tied black plastic garbage bag.

People who saw a neatly tied garbage bag have a strong sense of self-control. Maybe too strong. You hate to show weakness or make complaints—your pride won't allow it. But letting others know how you really feel is no sign of weakness. Loosen up the drawstrings and let in some air before all that garbage goes bad and starts to smell.

Abracadabra, Ala-Kazam

Playing cards that dance through the air . . . rabbits produced from a silk top hat . . . a lovely assistant made to disappear in a puff of smoke. Stage magic is simple deception raised to the level of entertainment. As you watch the performance, you know you're being tricked, but no matter how hard you think about it or how closely you watch the hands, it seems you can never put your finger on the secret. But somehow the witty banter and the sleight of hand make it all fun, and you sit back and enjoy the display of baffling skill. Perhaps the most important part of the magician's act is not in the mastery of the actual techniques or the preparation of the props, but in the ability to make an audience willing to believe.

Wouldn't it be nice to have that same skill? Well, tonight is your big chance. Your audience is waiting, and the curtain is about to rise. . . .

1. You are a stage magician, just setting off on another long tour. Tonight is opening night, and you are waiting in the wings of the stage for your act to be announced. How do you feel in the moments before your show begins?

2. Part of your act involves calling a member of the audience up on stage to help you with a trick. Whom do you call to assist you? Give the name of a person you know.

3. Despite all your years of training and experience, somehow the trick goes terribly wrong. What do you say to the person you called up to participate?

4. You're back in your dressing room after your act. How do you feel now that the show has ended?

KEY TO ABRACADABRA, ALA-KAZAM

(F) eats of magic are called *tricks* for a reason. They necessarily involve making people see things that aren't really there or miss realities that are staring them in the face. Essentially, tricks involve deception and guile. And the way you pictured your own performance shows how you see yourself when it comes to lying to or deceiving others, especially the people closest to you.

1. Your feelings as you waited to go on tell us how you would feel when planning (or merely fantasizing about) an illicit affair. Most people say something like "I hope I don't mess this up" or "Wow, I'm really nervous." But then there are those who seem to be immune to performance anxiety: "I'm gonna go out there and give them a night to remember!"

2. The person you asked to join you as your helper on stage is someone you see as simple, naive, and just a little bit gullible. In short, it's someone you think is easy to deceive or lie to. If you happened to name your current partner, it would be a good idea now to reassure him or her that of course you'd never do anything like that in real life.

3. The words you said after flubbing your act reveal the types of excuses you'd make if you got caught cheating.

Did you get flustered and turn red before blurting out, "Sorry, 'bout that."

Or did you just try to laugh it off and get on with the show: "Whoopsy daisy! Well, I guess that goes to show nobody's perfect!"

Or are you of the group that tried to pretend it was just part of the act? That'd be a neat trick if you could really pull it off.

4. The way you felt after the act was finished is the way you feel after doing or saying something dishonest.

"That was nerve-racking. What a mess!" That'll teach you to go around tricking people.

"That settles it. I'm getting out of this business." There are plenty of more satisfying careers for an honest, hardworking type. You're probably not cut out for all this smoke-and-mirrors stuff anyway.

"I'll get it right next time." Some people never learn. You may want to think about getting into politics, law, or used-car sales.

"Actually, I thought the whole experience was kind of stimulating." They say that once a fox has had its first chicken, it never forgets the taste.

IN THE PAGES OF A MAGAZINE

Y ou've just bought a copy of a popular weekly magazine and taken it home to read. How do you go through the features inside?

1. Read the whole magazine in order from first page to last.
2. Jump straight to the articles that you know will interest you and read only them.
3. Flip randomly through the pages and read anything that seems worthwhile.
4. As long as the format hasn't been changed, you'd read the features in the same order as you always do.

KEY TO IN THE PAGES OF A MAGAZINE

(Y) our average weekly magazine represents the collected effort of a great many writers, designers, photographers, and editors offering a spectrum of opinions and points of view. It is an omnibus of the human experience, and your magazine reading style reflects how you confront that diversity of choices. In particular, the way you budget your reading time reveals your approach to handling resources, especially money.

1. Read the whole magazine in order from first page to last.

You're the type who knows where every penny of your money is and what it's being spent on. It's not that you're all that concerned about your budget or financial planning; you just feel more comfortable when you know exactly how things stand. You hate the thought of missing something, so you keep all your accounts in order and know the current balance of your checking account, including interest, as a matter of course.

2. Jump straight to the articles that you know will interest you and read only them.

Money burns a hole in your pocket. If you have it, you use it to buy whatever catches your fancy and think, Maybe I'll start a savings account next month, as you spend your last dime. If you have managed to save something, it's not unusual for you to make a trip to the cash machine and make a withdrawal just to give you something to do.

3. Flip randomly through the pages and read anything that seems worthwhile.

You'd say you're economical. Some would call it stingy. The fact is you don't spend frivolously or waste your resources, preferring to save it for a rainy day. You'll never get carried away with impulse buying or max out your credit cards shopping on cable TV, but you might want to loosen up those purse strings on occasion. After all, money is there to help you live well.

4. As long as the format hasn't been changed, you'd read the features in the same order as you always do.

You keep spending according to habit regardless of changes that take place in your life. If you hit the lottery, it would be hard for you to stop shopping at discount stores. Alternately, if you were facing bankruptcy, you might still insist on designer label clothes. You can't be bothered worrying about the vagaries of fortune, which would make it a good idea for you to hook up with a partner who can, and let him or her handle the finances.

UNDER A CLEAR BLUE SKY

I magine a clear blue sky without a cloud in sight. Just thinking about it should give your spirits a little lift. Now turn your mind's eye down to survey the landscape. Which of the following scenes feels most calming and relaxing to you?

1. A white snowy plain.
2. A blue seascape.
3. A green mountain.
4. A field of yellow flowers.

KEY TO UNDER A CLEAR BLUE SKY

(T)he color blue has power to soothe the soul. Even a blue image in the mind can slow the pulse and make you take a deep breath. Other colors have significance, too. The scene you pictured contrasted against that clear blue sky reveals a hidden talent that resides in the depths of your untroubled mind.

1. A white snowy plain.

You are blessed with a special sensitivity that allows you to comprehend situations at a glance and decipher complex problems without needing any proof or explanation. You have what it takes to be a clear-sighted decision maker and even something of a visionary. Always trust your first intuitions; they will guide you well.

2. A blue seascape.

You have a natural talent for interpersonal relations. People respect your ability to communicate with others and the way you help bring diverse groups together. Just by being around, you help others work more smoothly and efficiently, making you an invaluable member of any project or team. When you say, "Nice job. Keep up the good work," people know you mean it. So it means that much more to them.

3. A green mountain.

Your gift is for expressive communication. You always seem to be able to find the words to express the way you feel, and people soon realize it's exactly how they were feeling, too. They say that joy shared is multiplied, while shared grief is divided. You always seem able to help others find the right side of that equation.

4. A field of yellow flowers.

You are a storehouse of knowledge and creativity, bursting with ideas and almost infinite potential. Keep attuned to the feelings of others and never stop working on building your dreams, and there is nothing you cannot achieve.

INTO THE DEPTHS

Every adventure involves an element of danger—it's the danger that makes adventures so exciting and hard to resist. People willingly spend good money to experience that same thrill without the physical risk. It's this fact of human nature that keeps haunted house attractions and sky-diving schools in business. The impulse to face risks is in us all. Indeed, the fascination with danger can prove to be such a powerful lure that some people will gamble with their own lives to confront a mystery or explore a new world. We've all watched as the unwitting hero of a horror movie is about to walk through a darkened doorway and wanted to yell, "Don't go in there! Are you crazy?" But what would you do if it was you?

Our next scenario leads us into that dark world, where the line between simple thrills and actual fear is blurred. . . .

1. You are in an old, abandoned building where no human has set foot for years and have discovered a staircase leading underground. Slowly you make your way down, counting the steps as you go. One step . . . two . . . three . . . How many steps is it to the bottom of the stairs?

2. The underground room is pitch black. Then, from the darkness you hear the sound of another person. Is the person weeping softly? Moaning wordlessly? Is it a voice speaking to you?

3. How do you react on hearing the sound of this other person? Do you try to search out the source? Is your first instinct to run up the stairs without looking back? Or are you paralyzed with fear and frozen where you stand?

4. You hear a person now calling your name and see a figure descending from the light at the top of the stairs. Who is this person coming down the stairs?

KEY TO INTO THE DEPTHS

A bandoned buildings and underground rooms are highly symbolic of buried memories and old psychological scars. All of us have had an experience we'd rather not recall or a heartbreak we thought we'd forgotten. But the memory is not so easily erased, and the things we hoped to forget linger for longer than we'd like to admit. Your responses to this situation show how you deal with painful memories of the past.

1. The number of steps to the bottom of the stairs indicates the impact of the psychological scars you are bearing.

People who said there were only a few stairs feel little adverse effect from the past. But those who described a long staircase leading deep into the earth carry correspondingly deep wounds inside.

2. The sounds you heard out of the darkness reveal how you got through bad experiences in your past.

Those who said they heard weeping have been comforted by others in times of trouble and recovered with the help they received. The people who took care of you in their kindness have helped you become the person you are today. The tears you cried were not in vain.

People who heard wordless moaning went through the hard times in their past alone. The moaning you hear in the dark is your own buried pain. Perhaps the time has come to open the door and let the sun shine in. Things won't look so bleak in the light of day.

Those who heard a voice speaking to them wear their old scars like a badge of honor, refusing to think of them as wounds. Nietzsche said, "That which does not kill us, makes us stronger," and you seem to have taken this philosophy to heart. But be careful not to let this harden you to the feelings of others.

3. Your reaction to the sounds in the darkness shows how you deal with the painful aspects of your own past.

If you went out to search for the source of the sound, it's likely you show the same take-charge attitude in your own life. By facing your problems head-on, you're bound to discover solutions.

Those of you who ran straight back upstairs without confronting the sounds have a history of ignoring problems in the hopes that they'll just go away. That approach may work sometimes, but don't be surprised when trouble stays around longer than you anticipated. Sometimes you need to stand and face your fears.

If you were frozen in place with fear, it may be that you have unresolved conflicts in your own past that continue to haunt you and keep you from moving ahead with your life.

4. The person who appeared at the top of the stairs calling your name is someone you feel you can rely on in times of trouble. The name you gave is the person you believe will comfort you and help to heal your inner wounds.

IN THE BAG

A ll of us lose things. Sometimes we don't even realize they're lost. Think about the last time you lost something: that sense of frustration as you retraced your steps, scanning the ground, looking under furniture, and sifting through the trash. Remember the feeling of desperation as you checked your pockets for the fifth time just to make sure you didn't miss it? Lost objects have a way of staying lost, only to turn up months after you've given up looking and forgotten all about them. Finding things lost by other people works the same way. You don't find dropped wallets in the street or lost purses on the train by consciously going out to look for them. If you find one, it's usually just by stumbling across it while you're doing something else.

You're walking down the street when you come across a closed black briefcase. There's no one else around, and when you open it to check for the owner's name, out spills a bundle of cash. What is your first reaction to this sudden windfall?

1. "Hey, this must be my lucky day!"
2. "Oh no, what am I going to do now?"
3. "I'd better take a night to think this over."
4. "God must have wanted me to have this."

KEY TO IN THE BAG

(Y) our reaction on finding the bag of money reveals how you would react if an attractive person suddenly asked you out on a date.

1. "Hey, this must be my lucky day!"

You have a childlike capacity for joy at your own good fortune. If more people could express their happiness like you, the world would be a better place.

2. "Oh no, what am I going to do now?"

It's normal to feel a little uncertain at times like these. But in the end the decision is all up to you. Take your time and think it over, but don't spend too long wringing your hands or someone else might just come along and snatch your good fortune out from under your nose.

3. "I'd better take a night to think this over."

Big decisions should be made with a clear head after a good night's sleep. There's a lot to be said for your policy of looking before you leap, but wouldn't it feel good every once in a while to cross the street without looking both ways? Sometimes you need to go with your instincts, even if it means taking some unacceptable risks. Love and danger go hand in hand.

4. "God must have wanted me to have this."

Either you don't take divine intervention very seriously, or you think of dating as a religious experience.

CINDERELLA STORY

T he rags-to-riches story of a girl whose dreams come true, Cinderella is one of the classic fairy tales in world literature. Of all the memorable scenes in the tale, which stands out most in your mind?

1. Cinderella suffering at the hands of her wicked stepmother.
2. Cinderella being transformed into a beautiful princess by her fairy godmother.
3. Cinderella losing her slipper on the steps to the palace as the clock strikes midnight.
4. The scene where the prince finally finds her and fits the glass slipper on her foot.

KEY TO CINDERELLA STORY

(W)hy do you react so strongly to the scene you picked? A closer look at the elements of each scene tells us your choice is related to your greatest character weakness or flaw.

1. Cinderella suffering at the hands of her wicked stepmother.

The thought of poor Cinderella scrubbing the floors while her stepmother and sisters showered her with abuse evokes strong feelings of pity. But on the underside of pity lie feelings of superiority and pride. You remember this scene for the way it made you feel better than someone. It's good for you to be able to look down at others with a tender eye, but be wary of your tendency to look down on them all the time.

2. Cinderella being transformed into a beautiful princess by her fairy godmother.

With a wave of her magic wand, her fairy godmother makes Cinderella into an enchanted princess and changes her world forever. But here in the real world, things are not so easy to do. Your biggest faults are your blindness to the practical questions in life and your lack of attention to planning and consequences. You seem to forget that there are no fairy godmothers waiting to save you from the problems you create for yourself.

3. Cinderella losing her slipper on the steps to the palace as the clock strikes twelve.

This scene left a strong impression on you because it played upon your sense of dependency on others. It's easy to see yourself running out at the stroke of midnight, leaving behind nothing but problems and unanswered questions. In the short term, relying on others to clean up your messes may seem like the easy way through life, but one day you're going to have to face the music.

4. The scene where the prince finally finds her and fits the glass slipper on her foot.

Almost everybody loves a happy ending, and you count yourself among them. And therein lies your problem. You're too easily satisfied with the simple, the normal, and the average. All you expect from life is an average job, an average salary, average friends, average family, average kids . . . Work on discovering more of what makes you unique and original. Remember, you're an individual, even if you don't feel like one.

(Not So) Happily Ever After

airy tales have happy endings. They're supposed to, anyway. But what would you do if the happy ending you were waiting for didn't turn out as expected?

Picture yourself as Cinderella, standing by as the handsome prince tries to fit your lost slipper on your wicked and ugly stepsister's foot. Then imagine seeing her ecstatic grin as her foot slides in effortlessly—a perfect fit! How would you react to this unpleasant surprise? Describe in detail how you'd feel and what you'd do about it.

KEY TO (NOT SO) HAPPILY EVER AFTER

I n the story, the glass slipper represents the one thing Cinderella believed to be entirely and forever hers and hers alone. When you imagined yourself in her place, you took on that same set of feelings. The way you reacted to the unpleasant surprise ending shows the way you'd respond to a rival in love who tried to steal your partner from you. We all like to think our partners belong to us completely, but there are many ways of expressing that in action. What did you do to get back what was rightfully yours?

"I'd make the prince let me try on the slipper, too." You're not afraid to let your partners shop around a little before accepting that you're the only one for them. That's admirable self-confidence, but what are you going to do when the prince decides there's a whole kingdom of feet he hasn't tried that slipper on yet?

"I'd just accept it as bad luck and get on with my life." Having patience is a sign of wisdom, but sometimes you have to fight to hold on to what belongs to you.

"I'd grab that glass slipper and crack my ugly stepsister over the head with it." It may feel good to express your natural resentment, but the prince might not think much of his future bride getting into a catfight.

UNTAMED

When you see a tiger or leopard at the zoo, you can't help feeling it looks a little tame, as though something in its wild nature has been lost. Even huge creatures like elephants or grizzly bears seem diminished when they're locked up in a cage. That may be the reason safari parks have become so popular. The impact of seeing wild animals is so much greater when you can watch them in their natural state, and the thrill is that much more when only a thin car window stands between you and a hungry lion.

You are on a safari park tour, following the road through the open savanna. A short distance from the trail, you see a lion and lioness feeding, hungrily tearing at and devouring hunks of raw meat. What are you thinking as you watch this scene of untamed savagery?

KEY TO UNTAMED

A safari tour allows you to observe dangerous wildlife from a safe and protected distance, and the lions feeding represent a scene of natural forces unleashed. Your reaction to the scenario shows how you reacted (or would react) on seeing an adult video for the first time. What was your response?

"Wow! Look at them go! Hey, I'm getting a little hungry, too." That doesn't take much interpretation, does it?

"I don't want to watch that—it's disgusting." Nobody said it was going to be pretty.

"I'm scared." It's natural to be a little bit frightened, but you're safe as long as you stay on this side of the glass.

"Oh, give the poor things some privacy." You're truly a decent person, but are you sure you don't want to watch just a little bit longer?

MIDNIGHT CALLER

A s you fall sleep, you enter what could be called another world, as far from this one as any distant star. In that remote space, even familiar voices and sounds seem alien and strange. It is a world utterly removed from the one where we spend our waking hours, a world where the mind is free to roam.

You are lying in bed in that foggy zone between consciousness and sleep when the telephone at your bedside rings. It takes a tremendous effort to reach out for the receiver, almost as if you were moving underwater. You fumble to get the right ends aligned with your mouth and ear and manage to mumble, "Hello?" Who is the voice on the other end of the line, and what does that person say to you?

KEY TO MIDNIGHT CALLER

$\left(\text{B}\right)$ eing awakened suddenly from a slumber is disorienting and sometimes a little bit scary. It's a natural instinct to turn to others for help when you're confused or afraid. So although the ringing phone is the cause of your confusion, the voice you hear on the line is actually someone you depend on in difficult times.

Whom did you name, and what words of reassurance did they offer you?

Was it a familiar voice saying, "Hello? It's your mother. How come you never call me?" Well, you can always depend on mothers for that.

Or was it just a friend calling to talk for no special reason? Sometimes that's the best kind of reassurance when you're feeling scared.

WHALE WATCHING

ou are standing on the deck of a small whale-watching boat. The great blue ocean surrounds you on all sides as far as the eye can see. The salt spray mists your face as you lean over the rail to try to catch sight of these mysterious creatures of the deep. And then there they are—a family of whales has surfaced just a short distance away!

Which of the following best describes the family?

1. A small baby whale swimming behind its gigantic mother.
2. A baby whale snuggling close to its mother's belly.
3. A father and mother whale swimming with their baby.
4. A baby whale blowing a water spout as it swims off alone.

KEY TO WHALE WATCHING

$\left(T\right)$ he whale is a common instance of Jung's "Great Mother" archetype. The relationship you imagined between the whales in this scene is linked to the feelings you have about your own relationship with your mother.

1. A small baby whale swimming behind its gigantic mother.

The role of the mother is almost overwhelmingly important to you. It may be that your own mother is influencing the way you act and think even now that you're an adult. It might be a good idea to cut away some of those apron strings and work toward a new level of independence. After all, your mother didn't raise you to be a child forever.

2. A baby whale snuggling close to its mother's belly.

You crave physical affection. It's natural and normal to feel the need for human warmth, but you feel that need more than others. Men who gave this answer should be especially careful not to look to their partners to play the role of the surrogate mother—playing Mommy's little boy is no way to run a mature romance.

3. A father and mother whale swimming with their baby.

You have an equal appreciation for the roles of both your mother and your father (the father is often forgotten about in these types of imaginary scenes). As a child, your home life was most likely happy and secure, and the result is your balanced outlook on life.

4. A baby whale blowing a waterspout as it swims off alone.

You have achieved personal autonomy and are well on your way to real growth as an individual, but your insistence on being your own person can sometimes make you appear to be willful, headstrong, or just plain selfish. Take care not to be so individualistic that you alienate the people around you.

BLOWING YOUR OWN HORN

Humans aren't the only entertainers in the animal kingdom. We've all watched the horse shows in a circus, the tumbling bears, and the antics of chimpanzees on tricycles. Then there are the star performers of the watery world—dolphins, killer whales, and, let's not forget, the seals.

You are a seal in a marine park show, performing in front of a sellout crowd. What runs through your mind as you face out into the audience, pumping your horns and waiting for the next bucket of fish from your trainer?

KEY TO BLOWING YOUR OWN HORN

(T) rained animals performing in a show are doing a kind of forced labor, with no option of quitting midway. The thoughts you said went through your head on stage correspond to the feelings you have about your own job. The things you said to yourself are things you're really thinking while you're at work. What did you have to say?

"Can you believe these idiots are actually paying to see this?" You'd be surprised what the entertainment value of your efforts is to an outside observer.

"Hey, buddy, how about some salmon next time? If I have to eat another sardine, I think I'm gonna puke." Rephrase that sentiment and tell it to your boss the next time you're up for a salary review. The squeaky wheel gets the grease.

"This is so humiliating. I can't believe I'm doing this where all these people can see me." What was it you said you do again? Maybe you should look into a nice relaxing job in accounting.

PLANTING THE SEEDS

T he human spirit loves a challenge. This desire to overcome may be the secret to our success as a species. Every human science was born through hard study and failed experiments; and every human personality is the product of an innate drive to create something unique from one's raw individual experience. The need to be challenged is so strong in us that we sometimes make things more difficult than they need to be, just so we can rise to the occasion and overcome the obstacles we have ourselves created.

You are an eminent scientist who has been working to develop a new species of plant. You have spent years in your laboratory experimenting, and now your efforts have begun to show results. As the ultimate test of the hardiness of your creation, you plant 100 seeds of the new strain in an inhospitable desert location.

How many of those 100 seeds sprout? (Give a number from 0 to 100.)

Key to Planting the Seeds

(T) he number you gave as an answer correlates to your self-confidence level. In this story, the scientist stands for feelings of confidence and even pride. On the other hand, the hostile desert sands represent a difficult challenge or test and therefore elicit feelings of doubt and uncertainty. People who answered with higher numbers felt greater affinity with the scientist and have high confidence levels. Those who answered with lower numbers felt the challenge was too great and have correspondingly lower self-confidence.

Scale

99–100. It's an understatement to say you're self-confident; maybe a better word would be "vain." Sure, it's important to believe in yourself, but you tend to dismiss the challenges of the rest of the world. Don't forget that one of the truest signs of strength is accepting one's own weaknesses.

81–98. You radiate confidence in yourself and your own capabilities, but somehow it doesn't come across as arrogance. Those around you generally feel it as a sense of cool certainty, making you a natural leader wherever you go.

61–80. Maybe you're best described as a cautious optimist, hoping for the best but always prepared for the worst. That realistic philosophy keeps you grounded when others might lose their heads in the clouds.

41–60. Your self-confidence is in the average range—neither too cocky nor too unsure. Maybe you're still finding out what it is you're best at, or maybe you just have a healthy respect for the difficulties that stand before you. Believe in yourself and the world will follow suit.

21–40. While you don't doubt yourself entirely, you tend to overestimate the challenges confronting you. You may excuse this tendency as a simple resignation to the facts, but your pessimistic outlook affects the way other people see you. The only way for you to inspire confidence in others is first to have it in yourself.

1–20. It's one thing to be humble, but you need to focus on developing a better sense of your own value. There's nothing wrong with believing you can achieve great things, and with a little hard work you can. The only thing holding you back is you.

0. What looks like an utter lack of confidence is actually a sign of perfectionistic pride. You can't tolerate the thought of being proven wrong or even making a mistake, so you pretend that everything is too difficult for you. If you don't learn to face those fears, you may fool the world into thinking you're just a ne'er-do-well, but you'll always know that you never even tried.

THE STOLEN BERRIES

E veryone likes a nice person, and most of us try to be good in our own lives. Why is it, then, that there are so few people in the world who are good all the time? As hard as you may try, there are always those rotten days and moments of weakness where it just feels better to be bad. Whether that takes the form of driving too fast on the highway, cheating on a test, or "liberating" a box of pens from the office, we've all done things we can't be proud of or justify. The key to becoming a truly good person is in accepting the bad parts of your own personality and admitting that you're not perfect, not in trying to act like a saint while the devil on your shoulder whispers in your ear. We all succumb to temptation sometimes. But in the next scenario you might just get caught. . . .

1. On a stroll through the countryside, you come across a field of delicious-looking strawberries. Your stomach starts to rumble, and there's no one else around. Only a fence stands between you and a free lunch. How high is that fence?

2. You sneak into the garden and begin to help yourself to the fruit. How many berries do you eat?

3. Suddenly the farmer whose berries you're stealing appears out of nowhere and starts yelling at you. What do you say in your own defense?

4. After all is said and done, how did the berries taste? And looking back, how did you feel after your berry-stealing adventure was over?

KEY TO THE STOLEN BERRIES

(S) trawberries—seductively juicy and red—are a common symbol of sexual attraction and desire. The way you envisioned this scenario helps us to understand your attitude toward forbidden romance and stolen love.

1. The height of the fence you imagined around the field is a measure of your own level of self-control and resistance to sexual temptation. The higher the fence, the greater your own defenses. People who imagined a total enclosure exercise admirable restraint. Those of you who said it was only a string tied around some beanpoles at about knee height run a higher than average risk of getting burned by the flames of love.

2. The number of berries you said you would steal is the number of people you can believe yourself in love (or lust) with at any given time. If you said you'd quit after eating just one, you're likely to be faithful in your own love life as well (or at least a devoted serial monogamist). Those of you who got into the double digits may need to think seriously about applying the brakes on your libido. Nobody can keep that pace up forever.

3. The excuses you made to the farmer represent the way you'd defend yourself if you got caught having an affair. What was your excuse?

"I'm so sorry. I promise I'll never do it again." Sometimes a full confession and a promise to behave is the best way to get yourself off the hook.

"They looked so good, I just couldn't help myself." Well, actually you did help yourself—to somebody else's berries. But honesty is the best policy. After all, it worked for George Washington, didn't it? If you keep it up, maybe someday you could be president, too.

"Hey those berries were great! Do you mind if I have a couple more?" Farmers have shotguns. Spouses have lawyers. Fortunately you still have a chance to reconsider your choice of words.

4. The way you described the experience and the taste of the berries gives an indication of how you imagine yourself feeling when looking back on a past affair.

"Actually, they didn't taste as good as they looked. The whole thing wasn't really even worth the effort." All too true for most affairs. Chalk it up to experience and put it behind you.

"So sweet! So juicy and delicious! I've never tasted anything like it!" Uh, let's just say you're addicted to love.

"The berries were nothing special, but all in all it was kind of fun." Statistically speaking, you're in the high-risk group for repeat offenders.

CAUGHT IN THE RAIN

Not everything in life is predictable. We're always getting hit by surprises, emergencies, and unforeseen disasters without any chance to prepare ourselves mentally. Surprises of any kind can be stressful—an unexpected proposal just as much as a sudden breakup. There are too many things we can't predict or control; that's one of the reasons we all tend to develop habits and patterns to live by.

You are walking outside when a hard rain suddenly begins to fall. Even if you run full speed, you're still about five minutes from your destination. Which of the following best describes your choice of action?

1. "I'd find an awning or tree to stand under and wait for the rain to stop."
2. "I don't know how long it's going to keep raining, so I'd run to where I'm going as fast as I could."
3. "I'd see if there was anybody around with an umbrella I could share or a store where I could buy one."
4. "I always have a folding umbrella in my bag when I go out, so I'd just use that."

KEY TO CAUGHT IN THE RAIN

(H) ow did you respond to the sudden downpour? The rain-
storm represents unforeseeable and uncontrollable forces
in life. Specifically, your answer shows how you tend to react when
a fight breaks out between you and a loved one or friend.

1. "I'd find an awning or tree to stand under and wait for the rain
to stop."

You're the type who waits for the other side in a fight to cool
off before trying to settle your differences. You prefer to let them
rant and rave until they run out of steam, then present your case
calmly and objectively. Some would say this is the intelligent approach, others would say it's just sneaky.

2. "I don't know how long it's going to keep raining, so I'd run to
where I'm going as fast as I could."

You don't care about the end result of a fight so much as getting to speak your mind. You're sure you're right, and there's no
sense in arguing the point. The concept of give-and-take doesn't
figure into your tactics. If they get angry, you get angrier. If they
start to yell, you scream. This doesn't make you much fun to argue
with, but at least it's easy to tell where you stand on an issue.

3. "I'd see if there was anybody around with an umbrella I could
share or a store where I could buy one."

You don't like conflicts and confrontations, so you try to smooth things over and calm the other person down whenever a fight breaks out. Unfortunately, sometimes that only makes things worse. It may be important for you to make a stand and weather the storm every once in a while.

4. "I always have a foldable umbrella in my bag when I go out, so I'd just use that."

You think you have an answer for every accusation, a justification for every fault. To you, an argument may be just a chance to hone your skills at debate, but to others you seem slippery, frustrating, and insincere. But of course, you probably have a good explanation for that, too.

ADRIFT ON THE BREEZE

C an you still remember those long summer days when school was out, you had no responsibilities, and there was nothing but time from when you woke up till the sun finally went down? Time for play and adventure, time to daydream and roam. Hours to spend on childhood diversions . . . flying kites . . . watching clouds . . . blowing bubbles . . .

Imagine you are out again on a childhood summer's day, blowing bubbles in an open field. Which of the following best describes the scene you imagined?

1. The bubbles you blow float away high into the sky.
2. You are blowing hundreds of tiny bubbles through your plastic ring.
3. You're concentrating on blowing a single enormous bubble.
4. The bubbles you make are carried behind you on the breeze.

KEY TO ADRIFT ON THE BREEZE

(T)he shimmering bubbles you blow in your imagination are symbols of your hopes and dreams. The scene you described reveals how you think about the dreams you hope someday will come true.

1. The bubbles you blow float away high into the sky.

You see your own dreams as elusive and unattainable, flying away from you like soap bubbles on the wind. Maybe you're wishing for too much, too soon or are caught up in an impossible fantasy. Whatever the case may be, the gap between your dreams and reality is wide. As much as you may like to tell others of your grand schemes and plans for the future, somewhere inside yourself is a voice telling you just how fragile and fleeting those dreams are.

2. You are blowing hundreds of tiny bubbles through your plastic ring.

You've set your sights on the immediate attainables—new clothes, a car, a boyfriend or girlfriend. Your dreams are sensible and always within your reach. Decide what it is you want most in the world and work for it. If you chase after everything at once, you stand a good chance of ending up empty-handed.

3. You're concentrating on blowing a single enormous bubble.

You have a single, all-important dream or ambition that drives your entire life. Hold on to that desire and keep striving toward your goal. Given time, you'll see that it's not so far from your grasp.

4. The bubbles you make are blown behind you on the breeze.

Your disappointing experience with unfulfilled hopes and dreams in the past shapes how you think today. But the experience of chasing after and losing a few dreams along the way was all just training for you as you make new goals for the future. Don't be afraid to keep dreaming—the only people who never fail are those who never try.

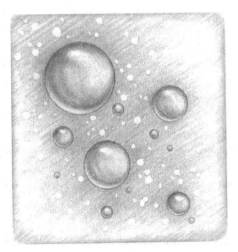

BARE NECESSITIES

T here are a few common items that people keep in their pockets or a bag nearly every time they leave the house: wallet, keys, ID, and credit cards. The insides of our bags are like the insides of our heads; we all carry around a lot of the same stuff, but there's always something in each one that makes every bag unique.

You're getting ready for the day and putting together your things. Besides the bare necessities, which one of the following items do you want to take along with you?

1. Your personal organizer or address book.
2. Hairspray or mousse.
3. A lucky charm.
4. Candy or gum.

KEY TO BARE NECESSITIES

$\left(\text{W}\right)$ hat is it you always want to have close at hand? The item you wanted to bring along is something you feel a little uncomfortable being without, and your choice actually tells us something about a part of your personality you feel insecure about.

1. Your personal organizer or address book.

You can't trust your memory. Phone numbers, birthdays, appointments; they run through your head like water through a sieve. You don't mean to forget things, but somehow they just never seem to stick, and you end up apologizing for missing your anniversary—again. It's probably a good idea for you to keep that address book with you all the time. Now if you could just remember where you left it.

2. Hairspray or mousse.

Appearances are all-important to you. That attention to detail means you always look great and ready to take on the world, but sometimes you take things too far. Remember, a bad hair day is not a valid excuse for calling in sick.

3. A lucky charm.

You're a firm believer in your own bad luck. The lines at the other tollbooths are always moving faster, your toast always lands jelly side down. Things never seem to go your way, and you've noticed. How couldn't you? It's not to say that you're superstitious, but you do feel a little more comfortable with your personal good-luck charm, whether it's a four-leaf clover, a St. Anthony's medal, or just a pair of old socks you've grown attached to.

4. Candy or gum.

You're worried about controlling your diet. Eating a pint of cookies 'n cream the day after starting a new diet, opening the door of the fridge every time you go past, "just to check"—your appetite fills your mind more than it does your stomach. Keeping some mints or a candy bar with you makes you feel safe. No matter what may happen over the course of the day, at least you know you won't starve to death.

SOMETHING'S FISHY

When it comes to relaxing in the great outdoors, few activities have the perennial appeal of fishing. Every weekend, no matter the weather, dedicated anglers set off for their favorite spots, joined by curious first-timers in their pursuit of the day's catch. Not many pastimes can boast the number of confirmed addicts that fishing has. What could be the secret of its allure?

You are out for a day of fishing when you get a strike. As you reel the fish up out of the water, it thrashes on the line and smacks into you. What area of your body does the fish hit?

KEY TO SOMETHING'S FISHY

(T) he fish you hooked acted out what could be interpreted as a final counterattack, and the place you imagined it striking is a part of yourself you particularly want to protect. It is a truth of human psychology that we often fantasize that those things we want to keep hidden will get found and the things we want to protect will come under attack. So the body part you named is actually a place you feel insecure or sensitive about.

Was it your face? Take a good look in the mirror. Maybe you just need to smile more.

Your stomach? Maybe your unconscious is telling you it's about time to cut down on the cheesecake.

Somewhere between the legs? Well, we all feel a little sensitive down there.

Welcome to My Parlor

I n the human unconscious, spiders hold a place of fear and respect that's entirely out of proportion to their tiny size. Perhaps it's their skill in hunting, their patience when lying in wait, or their ability to weave devious webs to trap their prey. Whatever the reason, spiders evoke a strong mixture of feelings in us all.

Imagine you are a spider, sitting at the center of a large web you have spun.

You will need a pencil and paper for this quiz.

1. Draw a picture of your web and the number and types of insects you have trapped in it.

2. You move to make a meal of one of your pray, but somehow it frees itself from the web and escapes. As it hurries out of reach, the lucky bug says something to you. What are its parting words?

KEY TO WELCOME TO MY PARLOR

(T) he spider is one of the great hunters of the natural world. Your impressions of life as a spider show us something about how you see your experience as a hunter in the wilds of love.

1. The number and types of bugs you drew corresponds to your own love conquests. The web represents your strategies and techniques for luring others into your clutches, while the types of bugs you caught reflect your opinion of your former lovers. Was it a single common housefly? A lovely butterfly that only leaves you hungry afterward? Perhaps a fat, juicy caterpillar? Or maybe an unappetizing mass of mosquitoes, roaches, and worms wriggling as they await your approach? Some spiders will eat anything.

2. The parting words of the bug that got away are your memories of rejection in a failed conquest. Let's face it, we've all been shot down at one time or another—this game shows the words that hit closest to home.

"You'll never catch me, you ugly old spider!" Ouch.

"Better luck next time!" Well, thanks for the encouragement, anyway.

"Hooray! I'm free, I'm free!" Okay, you're free. But you don't have to be quite so happy about it, do you?

YOU BE THE JUDGE

T he bang of the gavel, the slick attorneys matching wits, the hush that descends as the verdict is read—there are few movie settings more dramatic than a courtroom. It's a suspense-filled battle of intellects in which the line between right and wrong is often blurred and the link between law and justice can get lost in the scuffle.

If you were an actor playing in a courtroom drama, which of the following characters would you see yourself portraying?

1. The lawyer.
2. The detective.
3. The accused.
4. The witness.

KEY TO YOU BE THE JUDGE

(I) n psychological terms, the actor is associated with your so-cial persona (Latin for "mask"), the face you put on to deal with the outside world. Imagining yourself as an actor gives you the freedom to play the role as you truly see yourself. And the courtroom setting adds a sense of intensity and excitement to the scene. The role you saw yourself playing shows how you typically respond to a crisis situation.

1. The lawyer.

You normally keep your cool under fire and rarely let others see you sweat. But you also have a different face that surfaces only under the most intense pressure—a hotheaded fighter who's able to forget restraint and explode when the case demands it. This com-bination of cool readiness and fiery passion carries you through even the most desperate situations.

2. The detective.

You don't get swept away by chaos and confusion and always keep your head while others around you lose theirs. People sense and respect that imperturbability and tend to turn to you for help when they're in distress. This means that trouble seems to follow you, but you don't mind the added stress—in fact, it only makes you calmer.

3. The accused.

At first glance you seem tough and unconcerned, but underneath, you lack what it takes to see your battles through to the end. When things get tough, you waste time second-guessing and judging yourself instead of addressing the problems at hand. It's probably in your own best interest to ally yourself with someone who handles things more practically.

4. The witness.

You may look cooperative and helpful in any given situation, but your flexibility and eagerness to please also make you a source of another kind of trouble. By trying to get along with everyone all the time, you end up being inconsistent and even a little untrustworthy. Don't worry so much about whether your statements are making people happy or upset. The only thing you really have to prove is yourself.

Whispers in the Darkness

W hen you think of a bat, the first images that spring to mind are probably dark caves, night skies, and blood-sucking monsters. But although they're an object of many fears and superstitions, bats have another secret side. Despite their wings, they are mammals like us and nurse their young with caring and affection. And though they look fierce, the society of bats is more peaceful than our own. So the next time you see a bat flitting overhead, think that it may be looking down with the same fascination and dread that you feel.

You are lost in a deep cavern, wandering through a vast network of winding passages. As you search for the way back to the surface, a bat flies up and whispers something in your ear. . . . Which of the following does the mysterious creature say?

1. "I know where the exit is."
2. "Let me show you the way out."
3. "Keep looking."
4. "You're never, ever going to get out of here."

KEY TO WHISPERS IN THE DARKNESS

$\left(\text{I}\right)$n this scenario the magical bat serves as a symbol of guidance and aid for those lost and struggling. By imagining what the bat might say to you, you give an important glimpse at the way you yourself respond to others in need of your assistance.

1. "I know where the exit is."

You tend to be something of a busybody and a know-it-all. There's no question that you're always willing to lend a hand or a bit of advice, but you sometimes try to help when it's not needed, and end up looking like a meddler.

2. "Let me show you the way out."

Your big heart and selflessness serve as a shining example for others. People sense your strength and caring and are comforted just knowing you're around when a problem arises.

3. "Keep looking."

You keep your distance out of respect for other people's space. It's not that you're unhelpful, but you only give the absolute minimum when asked for advice and generally encourage people to work things out on their own. And that principle of noninterference may be the best long-term approach in helping others find their way to maturity and independence.

4. "You're never, ever going to get out of here."

When you see somebody who's down, your first impulse is to kick. It may be natural to feel a certain pleasure at other people's misfortunes, but that doesn't make it good. Your attitude isn't going to win you many friends or help you keep the ones you have. Watch out.

THE BIG BLOWUP

An erupting volcano is one of the most awesome displays of nature's fury, belching forth hot lava and poisonous smoke that can reduce the surrounding landscape to gray ash. The destruction it brings overwhelms everything in its path, and it's easy to understand how ancient civilizations could have regarded volcanoes as signs of the anger of the gods. Even today volcanoes seem to be sending us a not so subtle message about our place in the grand scheme of things.

You are standing within view of an erupting volcano. Which of the following best describes your thoughts at watching the spectacle?

1. "Maybe this is nature's way of warning us to stop destroying the earth."
2. "I guess the pressure just got too high inside there."
3. "Wow—what a sight! I'm impressed!"
4. "It's in the nature of these things to blow up. Big deal."

KEY TO THE BIG BLOWUP

(T) he thoughts you had about the volcano are linked to the way you react to explosive power, specifically the anger of a superior. We've all run into a boss, teacher, coach, or parent who throws the occasional tantrum—this scenario shows how you deal with those blowups.

1. "Maybe this is nature's way of warning us to stop destroying the earth."

You recognize when you're responsible for other people's anger and are willing to accept the blame. That same sensitivity and adult attitude lets you clear up any problems you might have caused.

2. "I guess the pressure just got too high inside there."

You place the blame for any problem squarely on someone else's shoulders. After all, if you thought you were doing something wrong, you wouldn't have done it in the first place, right?

3. "Wow—what a sight! I'm really impressed!"

You accept criticism and even outbursts in a positive way, but that's not to say you take them lightly. That sunny outlook is sure to make a favorable impression on superiors in the long run, after they've forgotten whatever it was they were yelling for.

4. "It's in the nature of these things to blow up. Big deal."

Strong words, tirades, and harsh critiques leave you unimpressed, probably because you don't listen to them. Sure, that's a low-stress way to get through a chewing-out, but you're running the risk of never learning from your own mistakes. Maybe you should start paying a little more attention to all that sound and fury; it might be signifying something after all.

IN BUSINESS FOR YOURSELF

T he crowded walks at a summer fair are lined with street vendors hawking their wares from tents and stands. Table after table of wooden children's toys, crafts, oil paintings, silver jewelry, and other treasures draw the eyes of passersby and make them pause a while to browse. Everything is made by hand, and no two items are alike, giving a sense of hope that a once-in-a-lifetime find waits unnoticed at the back of some counter display. The quality of the goods ranges from merely competent to exquisite craftsmanship equal to that found in the finest boutiques, and the vendors themselves, with their colorful personalities and appearances, add a dimension to the adventure that can't be found in any window-shopping experience. The scene has been set; why not stop a while and see what's up for sale?

1. You have opened a tabletop stand to sell your own original handmade jewelry. How many different types of accessories and bangles do you put on display?

2. A person walks up and looks over your table but after only a moment walks away without buying anything. What do you think to yourself?

3. Another potential customer comes up and seems extremely interested in one of your designs. In fact, you consider it the best

piece in your collection. What type of salesmanship do you use to recommend it?

4. It's time to close up shop for the day. How would you describe your sales?

KEY TO IN BUSINESS FOR YOURSELF

(F) ashion accessories like jewelry express the social side of the self. Items you make by hand only deepen that personal meaning and significance. Your responses to this scenario therefore show how you hope to be viewed by others.

1. The number of different kinds of jewelry you sell corresponds to the number of different personas or social masks you wear in different situations. These are the faces you put on in front of your friends, your parents, your boss, your partner. The more you have, the more complicated your social life will seem.

2. The feeling you had at losing a customer corresponds to your feelings after a heartbreak or other rejection. Did you feel it was something you did wrong ("I wonder what it was they didn't like?"), shrug it off and get on with your business ("No problem, there's plenty of other people in the park"), or take the chance to make some critical observations of your own ("They wouldn't know quality workmanship if it walked up and bit them on the nose!")?

3. The way you talked about your finest piece reflects what you feel your own strong points to be and the ways you try to express them to others. Did you take a low-key approach and let customers make up their own minds, hammer the point home by badgering them

incessantly, or offer to lower your asking price? Be careful not to sell yourself short.

4. Your sales total for the day is an evaluation of your own social achievement. Those who said they sold out their entire stock are not short on self-assurance. Just try not to scare people off with your boldness. If you said you had a bad day, you may need a little boost of self-esteem. Don't be too hard on yourself; customers can smell doubt a mile away. If you had average sales for the day, you're the type who understands your true place in the world without undervaluing your own worth. And that may be the key to achieving long-term success in this line of work.

Before They Hatch

F or most people, the word *egg* means a chicken's egg, and that means one thing: food. Scrambled, poached, or sunny-side up, mixed into cake batter, or gulped down raw—the variations are endless. Although we see eggs almost every day, there's something mysterious about them. Maybe it's the way they contain so much without having any seams or openings. Or maybe it's the promise of gold hidden within a plain white shell. Whatever it is—there's more to eggs than meets the eye.

Imagine an egg on a table in front of you. The egg may be of any shape, color, size, or species. You crack it open. What kind of egg is it?

1. A snake's egg.
2. A turtle's egg.
3. A dinosaur's egg.
4. A chicken's egg.

KEY TO BEFORE THEY HATCH

In addition to being an excellent source of protein, the egg is also a symbol of future generations and your own children. The type of egg you picked holds a special meaning about the hopes and wishes you have for your own children.

1. A snake's egg.

The serpent is symbolic of both wisdom and hidden wealth, which are the very things you want your children to have most. Keep a balanced perspective and remember that what your kids will want most from you is simply love.

2. A turtle's egg.

The turtle is universally seen as a symbol of health and longevity. Your main wish for your children is good health and physical wellness.

3. A dinosaur's egg.

The thing you most want is for your children to grow into unique individuals. You don't want them to be forced into the cookie-cutter molds of school, work, and society in general. They're bound to make mistakes; you just hope they make original ones. It's an admirable goal to have for your children, but keep in mind that one of the first steps children make toward independence is rebelling against their parents.

4. A chicken's egg.

You don't have any wild dreams or ambitions for your kids. If they're happy, what else really matters? The security and simple pleasures of a normal life will do. Just one word of practical advice: There's nothing wrong with having big dreams.

HUNG OUT TO DRY

I t may seem a little old-fashioned now, but it wasn't that long ago that hanging your clothes out on a line was the only way to get them dry. Now we're blessed with automatic dryers and wash-and-wear shirts, but it used to be you had to keep an eye on the weather when you were doing your laundry or face spending a day walking around in damp jeans.

You are back in the era when everything was washed by hand and hung out to dry. The dirty clothes have started to pile up, and you really need to do the laundry today. But when you look at the sky, you see dark clouds threatening rain. What goes through your mind?

1. "Oh no, you've got to be kidding! You mean I've got to wait till tomorrow? What am I going to wear?"
2. "Let's wait for a little while and see if the weather clears up."
3. "Well, I guess I won't have to do laundry today after all."
4. "I'm going to do this damn laundry whether it rains or not."

KEY TO HUNG OUT TO DRY

$\left(\text{W}\right)$ hen you add unexpected bad weather to the drudgery of household chores, you get a perfect example of the kinds of little stresses we face in our everyday lives. Your answer to this bad laundry day is a meter reading of the stress level you feel in your own life.

1. "Oh, no, you've got to be kidding! You mean I've got to wait till tomorrow? What am I going to wear?"

Stress level: 80. You've been letting all the little things that can and do go wrong in life get to you, and now the stress has built up so much that even the smallest annoyance can send you into a funk all day. It's time for you to take a break and relax before it starts affecting your health.

2. "Let's wait for a little while and see if the weather clears up."

Stress level: 50. You aren't overwhelmed by stress in your life, and you manage to keep a good perspective when things don't go as planned. Keep working on those problems you can solve as they arise, and you'll be fine. Remember, not all stress is bad. Let the stress in your life motivate you.

3. "Well, I guess I won't have to do laundry today after all."

Stress level: nearly 0. You don't let small problems bother you and don't see the point in worrying. You may be on to something with your easygoing philosophy; you can't stop the rain by worrying about it.

4. "I'm going to do this damn laundry whether it rains or not."

Stress level: close to 100. You feel so much stress in your life that you ignore reality and try to achieve the impossible. And when you fail, you end up with bigger problems and more stress than before. If you'd just take the time to relax and think things through, you'd see how much effort you've been wasting. Slow down and take things easier. It won't kill you to wear that same pair of socks one more day.

They say that the eyes are the windows to the soul, and that is true of animals as well as man. When you look into the eyes of a friendly dog, it seems to be begging you to play, while if you stare into the eyes of a cat, it looks back with cool indifference. Animals have feelings and personalities just like humans, and if we would only heed our eyes, we'd see how close our worlds really are.

You are strolling through a zoo, watching the animals in their cages. You stop in front of a single monkey in its cage and your eyes meet. The expression in its eyes seems to be communicating something. What is the monkey trying to tell you?

KEY TO LIKE A MONKEY IN A CAGE

(C) aged animals are mentally associated with the loss of freedom and the restraints placed on our natural instincts by society. And because they are humanlike in so many ways, it is particularly easy for us to empathize and identify with monkeys. The message the monkey was sending corresponds to your true feelings about the restrictions on your freedom. Specifically, they are words you'd like, but are unable, to say about a company, a group, or a social system that you feel is running your life. Do any of these answers sound familiar?

"Boy, I'd like a banana." You are easily pleased and, therefore, easily controlled. Hold out for more and you might be surprised at how much you're worth to others. Who knows, you might even get two bananas.

"All right, move along, nothing to see here." It's not the pressure of conforming to society's rules that gets to you so much as it is the lack of privacy. Don't be afraid to go off by yourself to be alone with your thoughts from time to time. You're only a single monkey; the zoo will survive for a while without you.

"I think I'm going crazy in this cage. Get me outta here!" As a licensed Kokologist, I'm prescribing you a long vacation on a nice quiet island. Take it.

THE GREATEST MYSTERY

Nobody really likes to dwell on the subject, but take just a moment now to think about what happens to us after we die. Does the soul move on to another world, or is death the absolute and final extinction of the self? Do you believe in heaven and hell or that the soul is reborn in a new body on earth? People have been wondering about these same questions for thousands of years, but in the end we have to admit that we just don't know. In this life, death remains the greatest mystery of all.

In this scenario, imagine that the soul survives after death. What form do you imagine it takes once it is freed from the body?

1. The soul is the same size and shape as its body was in life.
2. The soul retains its human form but expands in size.
3. The soul is tiny and human shaped, like a fairy.
4. The soul is like a ball of flame or a cloud, without definite form.

KEY TO THE GREATEST MYSTERY

(T) he image you have of the soul is a direct reflection of your own self-image. The nature of the soul you pictured shows how you feel about yourself.

1. The soul is the same size and shape as its body was in life.

You have one of the most valuable things in the world—self-esteem. You accept yourself, faults and all, and love yourself for what you are. Always keep that same attitude as you go through life, and keep discovering how much about you there is to love.

2. The soul retains its human form but expands in size.

You are not satisfied with yourself as things stand today. You feel there are so many things you've yet to experience and achieve, which makes you see the true self as much bigger than it is now. That dissatisfaction can be a source of inspiration if you learn to control it. Otherwise it will only haunt you as a sense of incompleteness.

3. The soul is tiny and human shaped, like a fairy.

Despite all your good qualities, you still have not discovered what it is within you that makes you great. It's not so much a feeling of dissatisfaction as it is of self-doubt. You tend to wonder, "What's wrong with me?" but you never seem to be able to put your finger on the answer. What's wrong with you is you're human, just like the rest of us, and that means imperfect. Accept that, and you'll begin to see that being human has its good points, too.

4. The soul is like a ball of flame or a cloud, without definite form.

You aren't upset by your shortcomings or proud of your strengths, and you can't be bothered in comparing yourself with others. In fact, you aren't very interested in issues of the self at all. That may be because you're incredibly shallow or because you're profoundly wise. But even that doesn't seem very important to you.

A TRUE ADVENTURE

H ave you ever had a true adventure, the kind you read about in novels or watch on the silver screen? An action-filled series of cliff-hanging scrapes and brushes with destiny, and of course a touch of romance to keep interest levels high? Wouldn't you like to?

1. You are a warrior in an ancient kingdom and have been chosen to accompany the most famous hero in the land on a mission to recover a stolen treasure. What does the hero say to you as you prepare to embark on your quest?

2. Before you set off, the king summons you and gives you a sword to see you through your adventure. What kind of sword is it? Describe it in detail.

3. Your travels take you over high mountains and through dense old forests, and you encounter many obstacles and crises along the way. Now you have finally arrived at the mouth of the cave where the stolen treasure lies waiting. How many enemies have you met thus far in the course of your adventure?

4. You enter the cavern and finally discover the treasure you have been seeking. At that moment, what expression crosses the face of

the great hero you accompanied on this quest? Describe the expression in detail.

KEY TO A TRUE ADVENTURE

(B) y entering the role of a warrior charged with a mission of great importance, you also assumed the associated feelings of pride in being trusted with such responsibility. Your answers to this quiz are linked to how you handle your own pride.

1. The words the venerated hero spoke to you are words that play on your pride. In a sense, the words you imagined the hero saying are words you have a weak spot for and that can spur you to action.

Did you hear something inspiring like "Trust me," "I'm counting on you," or "We're going to have to work together"? Each has its own special significance for the way you want to be called on for help.

Or was the hero something less than encouraging—"Just stay out of the way" or "If you're thinking about quitting, now's the time"? You have a soft spot in your heart for people with cold attitudes.

2. The sword the king gave you is a symbol of your own self-pride. Was it a finely crafted shining blade or a rusty, old, barely serviceable tool?

3. The number of enemies you encountered signifies the number of obstacles and crises you see yourself as having overcome in your own life so far. The greater the number, the greater your confi-

dence in your own abilities and pride in yourself should be. How many did you say?

Several hundred? One thing you don't lack is self-assurance. Of course, after all those adventures we're sure you have very valid reasons.

Just one or two? You don't see yourself as much of an adventurer, do you? Maybe you need some more life experience to help you gain confidence in yourself.

You didn't meet any enemies? Either the villains were too scared to show their faces after hearing you were coming, or you just figured they wouldn't bother with someone insignificant like you.

4. How did the hero react on recovering the lost treasure? The great hero who led you on this adventure actually represents those characteristics you admire most in the opposite sex (regardless of the gender you imagined the hero to be). The expression you pictured on the hero's face is the expression you find most attractive on a person of the opposite sex. Was it an ear-to-ear grin? A look of proud satisfaction or plain relief? Of maybe tears of joy? Whatever the expression, remember it. Someday someone may use it to unlock your heart.

MONSTER!

Monster! We all use the word, but who among us has ever seen one? Ask a hundred people to draw a monster and they'll paint you a hundred very different pictures. There are all kinds of monsters—the ones we see in movies, those that chase us through our dreams, the monsters of fairy tales, ghost stories, and even video games. They range from three-hundred-foot lizards to monsters in human form. What image does the word conjure up for you?

A monster is stalking the landscape, terrifying and unstoppable, and it is heading your way. This monster is out of control with rage and can't be talked to or reasoned with. But why is it so angry?

1. It's hungry and hunting for food.
2. It's searching for its lost love.
3. It's despondent because it's so ugly.
4. It's angry at the entire world.

KEY TO MONSTER!

(T) he monster in your imagination is a manifestation of the archetype known as the Shadow, representing the darker side to every person's personality. The Shadow is present in each of us, and the monster's anger is actually directed at a source of stress in our own life.

1. It's hungry and hunting for food.

The hungry monster is reacting to your own fight against your appetite. Have you been wrestling with a diet recently? It's hard to keep a clear head when you've got an empty stomach. Remember, everything in moderation, and that includes moderation itself. Better to have an occasional snack than to let the pressure build until you end up eating Tokyo.

2. It's searching for its lost love.

If you thought the monster was madly looking for its love, maybe you too have been going through some difficulties on the romantic front. Just keep reminding yourself, a love life without worries is no love life at all. Even Count Dracula had his off nights.

3. It's despondent because it's so ugly.

Those who thought the monster was consumed with rage at its own ugliness are dissatisfied with their own appearance in some way. Faults can become magnified in the mind's eye, and that negative self-image influences the way the rest of the world views us as well. The first step toward being loved is learning to love what you see when you look in the mirror.

4. It is angry at the entire world.

People who chose this answer have a pessimistic outlook. Not only is the glass half-empty, but the water is warm and tastes bad. It's good to be able to find mistakes that need correcting, but you'll never change the world just by complaining. Let's see if we can't find a way to put some of that energy to a more positive use.

THE LABYRINTH

L et's return once again to the amusement park to continue our explorations into the attractions of the unconscious mind. You're already familiar with some of the rides, the dizzying excitement of the roller coaster and the good-natured thrills of the merry-go-round. The house of horrors still lies waiting, but that's best left for couples to explore. How about a walk through the labyrinth instead?

You found your way through the giant maze and are standing at the exit. Which of these statements best describes how you feel?

1. "That was too easy. I was done in no time. What a piece of cake!"
2. "Well, it took a while to get through, but looking back, I guess it was really no big deal."
3. "Boy, was I lost! For a while there I thought I was never going to get out."
4. "I hooked up with a group of people inside and they showed me the way out. Otherwise I might still be in there."

KEY TO THE LABYRINTH

(T) he winding and circuitous paths of a maze represent the path you find for yourself in life, with all its false turns, backtracking, and dead ends. And adolescence is the time in life when it's easiest to feel lost and confused. Your experience in the labyrinth corresponds to the way you remember spending the years leading up to adulthood.

1. "That was too easy. I was done in no time. What a piece of cake!"

Although many people look back on their teenage years as a time of stress and confusion, for you it was nothing but fun. You weren't consumed with soul-searching or traumatized by peer pressure—actually the whole experience was like one big party. Of course, that may mean your true test in life still lies ahead. . . .

2. "Well, it took a while to get through, but looking back, I guess it was really no big deal."

Your school days were not easy for you, and it's more than likely you spent many a night worried over the same problems we all did—love, friendship, and the future. But that experience has helped to forge you into the person you are, and the lessons you learned will sustain you through any difficult times to come.

3. "Boy, was I lost! For a while there I thought I was never going to get out."

Although nearly everyone has a rough year or two growing up, you took worrying about life to the extremes, dwelling on problems that existed only in your head and torturing yourself with second guesses and self-doubt. That may have added a certain amount of seriousness and depth to your character, but now it's time for you to loosen up and enjoy life. You've earned it.

4. "I hooked up with a group of people inside and they showed me the way out. Otherwise I might still be in there."

The reason for the satisfaction you feel in life today lies with the friends you made and the relationships you formed during your youth. You had your worries like everyone else, but it seemed there was always someone for you to turn to when things got tough. Be grateful for the good luck you've had so far. Now it's your turn to return the favor and be there for others in need.

EMPTY INSIDE

S ome days everything just seems to go your way. Traffic seems to clear a path for you on the way to work; your boss takes the day off; you win the office pool. And you're all the happier because each new bit of luck comes as a pleasant surprise. Of course, there's another side to the unexpected as well. All it takes is a run in your stocking or a stain on your favorite tie to bring you right back down to grim reality. Good or bad, it's the little surprises that keep life interesting.

You go to a local bakery and buy a jelly doughnut. But when you get home and take a bite, you discover it's missing one essential ingredient—the jelly inside. How do you react to this bit of bad luck?

1. Take the defective doughnut back to the shop and get a new one.
2. Say to yourself, "These things happen," and eat the empty doughnut as is.
3. Eat something else.
4. Try filling the empty doughnut with something like maple syrup or jam to make it taste better.

KEY TO EMPTY INSIDE

Q: What do you call a jelly doughnut without any jelly in it?
A: A nasty surprise.

And while we're on the subject of the unexpected, you may be surprised to hear that the response you chose for this scenario shows the role you play among your friends.

1. Take the defective doughnut back to the shop and get a new one.

An orthodox thinker who isn't easily thrown off guard by odd occurrences, you can be relied on not to panic when the unexpected happens. But you aren't the type to take command and lead the way. Rather, you tend to support leader types with your clear judgment and coolheaded advice.

2. Say to yourself, "These things happen," and eat the empty doughnut as is.

You don't let surprises ruffle your feathers, accepting whatever hand the fates deal you. Your patience and flexibility make you incredibly easy to get along with, and it could be said you're the glue that holds your circle of friends together. Because you don't make a fuss over things, it sometimes seems that you fade into the background. But like air, you go unnoticed only until you're not around.

3. Eat something else.

Quick to make decisions and quick to act, you're a natural leader in any group. You come into your own when things get out of hand and the situation calls for one person to take charge and decide a course of action. You don't hem and haw over where to go for dinner or what movie to see—the word *indecision* is not in your vocabulary. That air of confidence and authority means that when you speak, the people around you listen.

4. Try filling the empty doughnut with something like maple syrup or jam to make it taste better.

Your talent for coming up with innovative solutions makes you the undisputed idea generator in your clique. Everyone has common sense, but you have a knack for uncommon sense that lets you see opportunities where others see only problems. Your creative instincts mean you run the risk of getting carried away with yourself and seeming eccentric from time to time, but people feel safe knowing that whatever may happen, you're sure to keep things interesting.

CIRCLE, TRIANGLE, SQUARE

Every shape and design may be reduced to the same basic building blocks: points and lines. For some, those words may dredge up painful buried memories of high school geometry class. But they can also take us back to a time when the world was simpler, to grade school art class when a house could be drawn using four squares and a triangle or a face created with a circle, two dots, and a wavy line. Our next quiz asks you to assume that innocent perspective and sense of creativity once more.

You'll need a pen and paper for this game. Using a single circle and any number of triangles and squares, draw a design on the paper.

KEY TO CIRCLE, TRIANGLE, SQUARE

(H) ow did your artwork turn out? Is it suitable for hanging on the refrigerator door? The real meaning of the design you drew can be found in your use of the three basic shapes. In this exercise the triangles represent work and study, the squares stand for society and its rules, and the lone circle is a symbol of yourself.

If you drew a very large circle, you possess an equally great sense of self. That can be a good thing when it leads to positive self-regard, but for some people it signifies a distorted notion of their place in the world—in other words, at its center. If you drew a very small circle, you see yourself as insignificant or dwarfed by the world around you. Don't let yourself be overwhelmed by all those triangles and squares; they're made of the same points and lines as you are!

The number and size of triangles you used represents your work or school responsibilities. Large triangles denote your sense of the importance of your work and the fulfillment you find in it, while a large number of triangles means you're working on several projects at once. Be careful if you have too many triangles; it may mean you need to cut down on your workload before it wears you out.

The squares in your design stand for how you feel about society and other people. If you used very large squares, it indicates you're under pressure to conform or fit in. If you put many squares in your design, it shows that you tend to feel lost in the crowd or burdened by too many rules.

If the shapes in your design connect, overlap, and share borders, it means you're enjoying a degree of integration and harmony between those aspects of your life. If all the shapes occupy separate spaces, it's likely you'll see signs of isolation and lack of connection in your life as well.

DOCTOR YOU

here's no escaping from desire. From the time we're children, we worry and want—I wish I were bigger, I want a new bike, I hope I don't fail the spelling test. The desire for a better life is in us all. And while it often leads to frustration and a sense of failure, that same desire is the driving force behind the successes we do achieve. Of course, no one succeeds in life alone. Everyone benefits at some point from a bit of wise advice, a kind word, or even a harsh critique. Think of all the times you yourself have been carried through a crisis supported by the words of others. If the time came for you to be the one giving support, what kind of job do you think you would do?

1. You are a psychotherapist with a private counseling service. In what kind of room do you hold your therapy sessions? Describe the room in detail.

2. Your first patient for the day has arrived. What problem does he or she want to talk over with you, and what kind of counsel do you give?

3. You sit across from the patient and give your professional advice. What kind of reaction do you get from the patient?

4. Office hours are done for the day, and you're at your desk doing paperwork when someone bursts in. Who is this person coming to you after hours? (Use the name of a person you know when answering.)

KEY TO DOCTOR YOU

(H) ow did you do with your caseload for the day? The patient in this setting expresses the part of yourself that longs for support and guidance. Your answers give a picture of the things you feel are missing from your life.

1. The type of office you described indicates something you feel is missing from your life. Did you envision a quiet room for privacy and deep reflection? A bright environment where it's easy to get things out into the open? Was it a comfortable, nurturing space where you could feel safe? Or simply a large room where you could stretch your legs and relax? Where is your mind telling you you need to be?

2. The patient's complaint is actually a source of worry in your own mind. Was it a problem in the workplace? A dead-end romance? Perhaps a quest for personal growth?

   The counseling you gave the patient is an answer to the problem facing you, from the clear-thinking, objective side of your mind. The question is, will you be able to take your own best advice?

3. The patient's reaction as you counseled shows whether you can accept good advice when it's offered to you. Was your patient hanging on every word you spoke or arguing with you stubbornly and refusing to take their own best interests to heart? Or did you

get the feeling that they were agreeing with what you were saying but would forget it all as soon as they stepped out the door?

4. The person who barged into your office after hours is the person in your life who causes you the most worry or stress. But that doesn't necessarily make that person a nuisance or someone to be avoided. Compassion for others is a mark of wisdom.

READY TO RUMBLE

Toe to toe in the ring, mountains of muscle and bone square off for the fight of the century. The wrestlers glower with menace and pace like caged beasts. The crowd roars with anticipation as its most aggressive fantasies are about to be played out.

No other sporting event has the elemental appeal of professional wrestling. We may laugh about it or shake our heads, but its popularity endures. If you had the chance to jump over that third rope, just for one night, what type of wrestler would you be? (Choose one of the following.)

1. A giant bruiser who bashes opponents into submission through sheer strength.
2. A technical wizard who invents elaborate clinches, drop kicks, and slams for each new opponent you face.
3. A villain type who resorts to illegal holds and banned objects every time the ref's back is turned.
4. An expressionless masked wrestler who never shows emotion or pain.

KEY TO READY TO RUMBLE

S ports are a socially acceptable expression of natural human aggression, but on a deeper level they also represent a sublimation of the sex drive. And pro wrestling, with its wild abandon, its glorification of the body, its raw humanity, and its naked aggression has closer links to sex than any other sport. The type of wrestler you said you'd become shows the type of partner you are in bed.

1. A giant bruiser who bashes opponents to submission through sheer strength.

You insist on having things your way. Like the fighter who reduces his foe to a quivering mass, you take control of your partners and bend them to do your bidding without a second thought. It may sound brutal and animalistic, but then we aren't talking about a game of tiddlywinks, are we?

2. A technical wizard who invents elaborate clinches, drop kicks, and slams for each new opponent you face.

You enjoy trying out new tricks and techniques with each new partner. Part of the excitement in the game of love is generated by the freedom it gives you to express your creativity. You love to home in on your partner's most sensitive spot, then go in for the kill.

3. A villain type who resorts to illegal holds and banned items every time the ref's back is turned.

You can't be satisfied in making love by the book. You're always looking for new sensations, and you're not afraid to break a few rules (or introduce some forbidden objects) to get what you want. Now, just put down that folding chair before somebody gets hurt.

4. An expressionless masked wrestler who never shows emotion or pain.

You don't like to reveal your true self, even in the most intimate encounters. There's an aura of mystery to your lovemaking style, an almost eerie sense of calm. This tactic can drive some partners wild with curiosity or leave them feeling cold. But there will always come the day when your mask is finally torn away. Are you prepared to confront the face concealed beneath it?

JUDGING BY ITS COVER

Think of what it would be like to be the best-selling pop star in the world, the darling of the media and idol to millions. It's not such an uncommon fantasy to entertain as you sing along to the car radio or belt out hit after hit in the shower. You get a thrilling sense of satisfaction from being able to move people through the power of song.

You are a new recording artist, and you've just finished cutting your debut CD. Now all that remains is for you to decide on a cover design for the CD case. What type of jacket design would you pick?

1. A soothing scene using imagery or photos taken from some exotic location.
2. A fun, cartoonish design or other playful image.
3. An abstract pattern without any obvious meaning, but one that makes people think.
4. A picture of yourself.

KEY TO JUDGING BY ITS COVER

(T) he idea of releasing your own CD ties into the psychological need for self-expression. The design you'd like to see on your CD corresponds to those aspects of your personality that you want others to take notice of. Your choice can be interpreted as what you see as your own best attribute. Now let's see how the rest of the world views you. . . .

1. A scene relying on imagery or photos taken from some exotic location.

You see yourself as a caring and gentle person who always has a smile or kind word for others. As a matter of fact, it's hard to imagine how someone could be more sensitive than you. But to others, it sometimes seems as though you've got a wall around you that doesn't let anything get through to you, and all that sensitivity starts to look a little insincere. If you never let your guard down and show how you really feel, people will always be wondering what you're really thinking.

2. A fun, cartoonish design or other playful image.

You're sociable, talkative, and fun to be around. And you know it. But others see the flip side of that coin as well—unrealiable, flighty, and tending to get carried away by the moment. Being able to make people laugh is great, but it takes on a different meaning if they're laughing at you, not with you.

3. An abstract pattern without any obvious meaning, but one that makes people think.

You take pains to express your natural creativity and talent to the world. That talent may be there, but you need to remember that other people have their talents, too. The real way for you to shine is to accept and work together with others. Until you do, you risk being seen as strange. Your originality is important, but don't let it make you into just another crackpot eccentric.

4. A picture of yourself.

You take the straightforward approach, saying, "This is me, take me as I am," and you see that simple honesty as your strongest feature. But what you intend as honesty can come across as stubbornness—"This is me, I'm never going to change." Nobody's so great that they can't get better. If you want to keep the same image forever, at least make sure they get your good side.

BUSTED!

They say that police develop a sixth sense about the criminal mind. And each of us has a little bit of that criminal mind inside, which is why the police can never afford to be off duty. Murder, robbery, fraud—they're even more common than the newspapers make it seem. Not a minute goes by without a crime being committed or planned. If you were a cop, how do you think you'd handle the pressures of the beat?

You're in hot pursuit of a suspect fleeing a crime scene. After a long chase, you finally manage to run him down and make the arrest. You're standing over him with your pistol in his face. Busted! What does the suspect say to you as he stares down the barrel of your gun?

KEY TO BUSTED!

W hat did the cornered crook have to say for himself? Although you were imagining yourself as the police officer, your own hidden tendencies came out in the criminal's words. In the game of cops and robbers, it's the robbers who have to come up with excuses as the cops haul them off to jail. The way you imagined him responding gives an idea of how you reacted when your parents caught you doing something bad. And if you're like most people, it's how you continue to behave today.

"Okay, I give up. You got me. I'll talk." It's good for the conscience, and they might go easier on you come sentencing.

"You think you got me? I don't see any evidence. I want to talk to my lawyer." You may be able to slip through the cracks once or twice, but your wicked ways will catch up with you if you don't reform. Justice never sleeps.

DRIVING MACHINE

R emember practicing for your driver's license and all the little things you had to learn? U-turns, parallel parking, hand signals, and car lengths. . . . Sure, they're all important, but that isn't what driving is really all about. Driving is about the way you felt after passing those tests and taking to the road all by yourself for the very first time. It's about being able to go where you want, when you want. It's about power, freedom, and speed. And the car you drive is an expression of the way you view the whole driving experience. It tells the world something about who you are and what you want out of life.

Take a moment to picture your dream car, without giving any thought to expense or other practical considerations. What kind of car do you envision yourself in?

1. A high-performance vehicle with all the options.
2. A marvel of design with a sleek and beautiful chassis.
3. A status-symbol ride with a price tag to match.
4. Anything will do as long as it runs.

KEY TO DRIVING MACHINE

(P) eople's taste in cars typically reflects their taste in members of the opposite sex. The features you want in your dream car reveal the things you respond to when looking for a partner.

1. A high-performance vehicle with all the options.

Ideally you want everything out of your car and your partner, but that also means you're willing to appreciate the good points in everyone. Your wide range of tastes means you might look a little inconsistent, equally attracted to beauty, kindness, sophistication, humor, or charm. But that makes it possible for you to evaluate potential partners on their own strengths, giving you a basis for comparison before making your final choice.

2. A marvel of design with a sleek and beautiful chassis.

There's little doubt that physical appearance is the key to winning your heart. It's not only finding someone whose looks appeal to you that's important. You also want someone you can show off to the world. The exaggerated emphasis you place on the exterior means it's easy for you to end up with a real lemon. Always check under the hood before you drive anything home.

3. A status-symbol ride with a price tag to match.

Social position and material success are crucial to you, and that carries over to your choice of partners as well. The right family, the right school, the right career: for you they all add up to make the right person. Ambition is not a bad thing in itself, but your mate might not appreciate being just another rung on the ladder to your success.

4. Anything will do as long as it runs.

You're happy with just about anyone who meets certain minimum standards, which makes you open, accepting, and forgiving. You don't expect others to fulfill your dreams and enjoy the same consideration in return. That could be a smooth road to contentment. But when you think about it, it might mean others aren't really expecting much from you, either.

JUST CAN'T WAIT

S tarting work at a new job is always stressful: the unfamiliar people and environment, the million new things to be learned, the feeling of wanting to do a good job, and of course the inevitable goofs. We learn by making mistakes, then trying not to repeat them.

A friend of yours has just taken a job waiting tables at a restaurant. One day you decide to visit and see how the new job is going, but when you step inside you see your friend has gotten into some kind of trouble with one of the customers. What did your friend do wrong? (Choose one item from the menu below.)

1. Didn't come to the table even after being called several times.
2. Made a mistake taking the order and brought the wrong food.
3. Spilled something on the customer's clothes.
4. Started to clear the table before the customer had finished eating.

KEY TO JUST CAN'T WAIT

(Y) our friend in the restaurant is a psychological stand-in for you. The mistake you saw your friend make is rooted in your own unconscious recognition of a personal weakness of your own, particularly in terms of responding to the needs of others. The mistakes you imagined your friend making are the very problems you find in your own love life.

1. Didn't come to the table even after being called several times.

You see yourself as lacking in the ability to concentrate and focus yourself on your partner. When out for the night, you might simply just wander away from your date when you see something that catches your fancy. Or maybe you're always getting caught with your eyes looking where they shouldn't be. That lack of focus might be interpreted as a lack of caring, so try to pay a little more attention. . . . Hello? Are you listening?

2. Made a mistake taking the order and brought the wrong food.

You come up short in the personal responsibility department. Maybe this manifests itself as always being late or in bringing along uninvited friends to what was planned as an evening for two. If romances are like a contract between two people, you've committed more than your share of breaches. If you want a happier love life, make a stronger policy of thinking about your partner's feelings before you do something.

3. Spilled something on the customer's clothes.

You're too nervous when it comes to dating. You want everything to be perfect and for everything to go smoothly, but it's difficult for others to relax when you make such a fuss over every last detail. You might make a good first impression by being so serious, but it's easy to see how people could quickly get tired of the high stress level.

4. Started to clear the table before the customer had finished eating.

You tend to jump the gun when it comes to love. That eagerness may seem charming at first, but after a while it just feels as though you're always chomping at the bit. Slow down and let your partner have a chance to breathe, or you may find yourself with nothing but time on your hands.

ON SECOND THOUGHT . . .

I t's not easy to make up a story, it's a chore to make up the bed in the guestroom, and it takes patience and forgiveness to make up after a fight, but sometimes the hardest thing to make up is your mind. Get ready to be decisive, because in this next scenario we're going to ask you to do just that.

You're seated in a quiet diner. You flip open the menu and are pondering your selection when the waitress arrives and asks if you're ready to order. Without thinking, you order a sandwich and a cup of coffee. But after she leaves, it comes to you—you're in the mood for hot chocolate, not coffee! What do you do next?

1. Keep looking through the menu and thinking about how good some hot cocoa would taste.
2. Look around to see if the waitress is going to come back.
3. Get up and find the waitress so you can change your order.
4. Give up and just wait for the coffee.

KEY TO ON SECOND THOUGHT . . .

G ranted, making a mistake when you order is not the end of the world. You'll probably have forgotten the whole thing a half hour from now. But the way you handled your mistake with the cocoa tells us something deeper about your personality. Your course of action (or inaction) shows how you would react to a relationship ending. Specifically it shows how long you carry a torch for a love gone wrong.

1. Keep looking through the menu and thinking about how good some hot cocoa would taste.

You're the type that doesn't know when to call it quits. You keep dwelling on the good times and fantasizing that someday things will get back to the way they were. Odds are they won't. The fat lady sang, and the curtain is already down. It's time to wake up and smell the coffee.

2. Look around to see if the waitress is going to come back.

You're not all that thrilled about the breakup, but you definitely don't want to make a scene. In a nutshell, you worry too much about what other people think. You're more concerned that people might be whispering about your getting dumped than you are about the actual breakup. Come to think of it, that pride of yours might have been the reason you got dumped in the first place.

3. Get up and find the waitress so you can change your order.

You're not the sort who gets mired down in romantic mourning and a sense of loss after a romance ends—mainly because it's completely inconceivable that that kind of thing could have happened to you. Your reaction is more a state of shock than mourning, and you'll do anything to try to make the memory go away. Maybe you should take up a hobby to take your mind off things.

4. Give up and just wait for the coffee.

Is that "Que Sera, Sera" playing on the jukebox? It might as well be, because that's your theme song. It generally takes you one night's sleep to get over a breakup. A power nap would probably do in a pinch. The question is whether that makes you thick-skinned, insensitive, or the most unshakable optimist in the world.

THE DOCTOR WILL SEE YOU NOW

A hospital means different things to different people. Those coming in to have some undiagnosed malady examined for the first time may look on the place with a sense of anxiety and dread. But for those walking out the door after recovering from a long illness or delivering a beautiful, healthy baby, the hospital takes on associations of happiness and relief. The hospital is a world in itself, where life and death, sadness and joy, cross paths and intermingle on a daily basis. And for the people within, every day is another chance to heal not just the body, but the mind as well.

Perhaps you have been to the hospital before, or perhaps this is your first visit. Either way prepare yourself, because the doctor will see you now.

1. You're in the lobby of a medical clinic, waiting for your name to be called. A small boy is racing around the waiting area unattended, and you warn him to be careful and slow down. How does he react?

2. The door to the examination room is open just a crack, and you catch a glimpse of a gray and unhealthy-looking person being examined by the doctor. The patient is a person you know. Who is it?

3. The doctor's aide comes out and calls your name. Strangely, the aide bears a very strong resemblance to someone you know. Whom does the aide look like?

4. After your examination, the doctor calls you into his office, but when you enter he remains seated with his back turned to you, muttering to himself as he goes over your chart. He shows no signs of explaining things to you. What do you do?

KEY TO THE DOCTOR WILL SEE YOU NOW

(T) he hospital is a place of sickness and healing. By visualizing yourself in this scenario, you tapped into those parts of your own psychology that feel weak or in need of care.

1. The boy's reaction shows how you react when others criticize you or notice your faults. Did he act as though he couldn't hear you, stop in his tracks and apologize, or stick out his tongue like a spoiled brat? Now you understand how other people feel.

2. The person you imagined as the patient on the exam table is someone you feel you could never rely on in a crisis. After all, how much help could they be if they look that much sicker than you?

3. The doctor's aide represents someone with the power to decide your fate. The person you thought the aide resembled is someone you have always looked up to, out of either fear or respect. No matter how strong you may someday become, that person will always be above you in your mind. It might have to do with the person's power to say, "Now drop your pants, bend over, and cough."

4. The way you responded to the doctor's behavior shows how you handle being bullied or teased. Some prefer to wait things out, others demand an explanation, and some just get up and walk out the door. What did you do?

Spreading Your Wings

In times of stress and frustration, it's normal and natural for people to want to shed their troubles and leave the world behind. Think about it. When you love someone who doesn't love you back, or things just aren't going your way at work, sometimes the easiest solution is to get as far away as possible until the feeling fades. Getting away gives you the chance to free your mind and do the things you want to do. But as much as we'd like to drop everything and walk out the door, it's easier to dream about than to do. Maybe that's what makes us turn to the heavens for relief—we all just want a chance to fly and be free.

1. You have decided to try skydiving and are getting ready to make your first jump. You watch other skydivers free-falling through the air as you stand on the ground waiting your turn. What is going through your mind?

2. Your turn arrives, and you ready yourself as the plane climbs to ten thousand feet. Without looking back, you stand at the open doorway and step out into space. What do you scream on your way down?

3. You've landed safely and are hauling in your chute when you see an instructor approaching and calling out to you. What is the instructor saying?

KEY TO SPREADING YOUR WINGS

(D) id you enjoy your little walk in the clouds? The pure adrenaline rush of a skydiving adventure relates to physical thrills of a different sort—the thrill of sex. The things you said about your parachuting experience actually describe your approach to lovemaking.

1. The way you felt as you waited your turn provides a measure of your own level of sexual desire.

"This is gonna be fun. I can't wait!" Sometimes it just feels right.

"I don't know if I can go through with this." If you're not sure you're ready, maybe you can just have a deep conversation and cuddle by the fire.

2. The words you shouted on the way down are what you would say at the peak of excitement.

"Wow, would you look at this view!" You may not mind the intrusion on your privacy, but you'd better ask your partner first.

"Maybe this wasn't such a good idea after all." There is such a thing as a point of no return.

"I want my mommy!" Um, let's just say you have some deep Kokological issues to work out and leave it at that.

3. The words the instructor said to you are what you imagine your partner saying after sex.

"Not bad for a beginner. Don't worry, you'll get better with practice!"

"Oh, I'm really sorry, I left the lens cap on the camera. Do you want to go again?"

"Well, I guess that about does it. Now, will that be cash, check, or charge?"

ALL THE WORLD'S A STAGE

L ife is often compared to a drama—it's an easy comparison to make. The coming and going of the characters, the suspense as each day's plot unfolds, the lines we hear spoken, and the acts performed: you could say we live each day on stage. There are even genres to the stories—office comedies and after-school specials, sometimes even a mystery or romance. And the star of each daily episode is . . . you! That's what makes life's drama so fascinating and endlessly varied—every cast member in every scene, every extra on the street, is the star of his or her own story in a plot that gets more complex every day. Even the simplest exchange between two people can have infinite implications as the drama plays out. Maybe that's why, despite the same old characters and story lines, we can never seem to get enough. In this next scenario the curtain is up, the crowd is waiting, and the spotlight is on you.

1. You are a member of a theater group. What type of play do you most want to act in? In the play, what do you picture as your big scene? Explain in detail.

2. You audition for the part and are chosen from among all your fellow performers for the starring role. What words does your main rival have for you on being chosen?

3. At the last dress rehearsal before opening night, you see the director sitting with his arms crossed in front of him. He looks dissatisfied with your performance. What is it he doesn't like?

4. The performance goes off without a hitch, and the play was a huge success. The crowd has gone home happy after the encore, and the theater is quiet. What do you say to the empty hall as you stand there looking out from the darkened stage?

KEY TO ALL THE WORLD'S A STAGE

(T)he theater represents a world of imagination you create for yourself. Your answers to this game reveal what lies waiting in your own future.

1. The type of drama you wanted to perform corresponds to your future. Did you foresee a melodrama, a tragedy, or a slapstick pie fight? And your big scene reveals what you predict will be the turning point in your life. If it was a love scene, there may be a romantic lead waiting to change your life. Was it a scene of parting with friends, of meeting new people, or of a heated battle? These all could be the cues for you to take center stage and make your command performance.

2. The image you have of your rival reflects how your future self might react to the person you are today. The rival's words give an idea of how you think you will feel while looking back on your life when you're older. Was your response something encouraging like "Nice going! Keep up the good work!" Or was there a sense of caution: "Don't get a big head. One good show doesn't make you a star. You've still got a long way to go till you make it to the big time."

3. The director watches every aspect of the performance with a cold and objective eye. His dissatisfaction was caused by a weak-

ness you unconsciously recognize in yourself. The flaw in your performance represents the area in which you're most likely to make mistakes in the future.

If he said your character was getting lost in all the scenery, you may need to work harder at standing up for yourself in life. Who's the star of this show, anyway?

On the other hand, if he told you that you were hogging the stage, you might want to try toning things down a notch. Nobody likes a ham.

If he told you your timing was off, be careful not to miss opportunities that come knocking in your life. There are no chances to redo a scene in the real world.

And if he said you just weren't exciting to watch, you should try to liven yourself up a little. If even you can't sit through your performance, think how the rest of the world feels.

4. Your words to the empty theater are the words you picture yourself saying at the end of your life. Recognize any of these famous last words?

"Thank God that's over! I need a drink!" An understandable sentiment, but there aren't any bars where you're headed.

"I couldn't have done it without the little people." It's good to remember the people who helped us on the way.

"That wasn't so bad." Maybe that's the best parting line that any of us can hope to be able to say.

"Look out, world, here I come." Just where is it exactly that you think you're going?

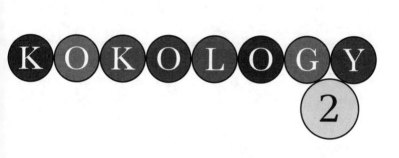

The Kokology Project Team

WRITERS	Tadahiko Nagao and Isamu Saito
EXECUTIVE PRODUCER	Hisataka Saito
GENERAL PRODUCER	Tadahiko Nagao Takanori Ikeda
COOPERATOR	Keiko Higashiomori
ILLUSTRATOR	Makoto Ishizuki
TRANSLATOR	Douglas Sipp, Office Miyazaki, Inc.
SPECIAL THANKS TO	James C. Vines Seiichiro Shimono Hisako Miyazaki Toshihide Ochiai Takeshi Itoh Hideaki Okada
SUPERVISOR	Isamu Saito

CONTENTS

CONTENTS

KOKOLOGY 101

kokology \ kō kŏl′ ō jē\ *n* [Japanese, *kokoro*, mind, spirit, feelings + Greek, *-logia*, the study of] **1.** A series of psychological games designed to uncover emotional and behavioral traits of the players **2.** A popular term for the interpretation of the hidden meanings of human behavior and situational responses — **kokologist** *n* — **kokological** *adj* — **kokologize** *vi*

A WORD FROM PROFESSOR SAITO

T he spread of information technology is helping to bring the world together. By exposing differences as well as un-covering similarities, global media promote mutual understanding among people of different cultural backgrounds. Of course, differences remain, but I believe that people are truly growing closer in their hearts and minds. So it has been gratifying to hear of the success of *Kokology* in the United States and across Europe. After all, Kokology is based on psychological principles that were first developed in the West, and it was originally intended to make those ideas more accessible to the general public in Japan. To see it return to its roots and meet with such widespread acceptance and popularity has strengthened my faith in the fundamentally universal nature of the human mind.

Kokology 2, like its predecessor, is intended as a tool to generate conversation and promote understanding, to help develop and deepen personal relationships, to spur the intellect and stir the imagination. But most of all, by revealing just how much we share, it shows that none of us is alone.

—ISAMU SAITO
Professor, Rissho University

INTRODUCTION TO *KOKOLOGY 2:*
KOKOLOGY AND YOU

You. It's a miracle that such a small word can hold such a range of meaning. Your face, name, and smile. Your body, mind, and soul. Your experiences and memories; your aspirations and your dreams. A billion attributes and inclinations constitute the unique individual summed up in those three little letters.

But despite your uniqueness, there are qualities shared by every "you" in the world. Illuminating the shared aspects of the human experience is what has made Kokology a worldwide phenomenon. Kokology is the study of you, in the broadest possible sense. Its universality has allowed a concept that began in Japan to open up new lines of communication between lovers and friends in countries around the world. The international success of Kokology speaks for the fundamental accuracy of its underlying assumption: that people want to explore the human mind and have a good time doing it.

Playing Kokology can be a little like rummaging around a dusty old attic. You may be reluctant to get started, but once the doors and windows have been opened, the air clears and the sun shines in. The experience suddenly turns into an adventure as things we thought we'd forgotten resurface in a new light.

We all have secrets locked up inside us, and we all have a desire to know and understand ourselves. But where is the person who can uncover those secrets? Who holds the key to unlocking the hidden world within? The answer, of course, is: "You."

—TAKANORI IKEDA
General Producer of *Kokology*

PLAYING THE GAME

When we set out to develop Kokology, our first and foremost goal was to make it fun. After all, who in their right mind would want to play a game that isn't? The basic concept was already there—our plan was to create a game where people would imagine themselves in everyday situations and unusual scenarios and respond to simple questions. The answers are interpreted from a psychological perspective and tell us something about the way that person's mind works. It's kind of like a Rorschach test that uses words instead of inkblots.

The concept was the easy part. The hard part was keeping the balance between science and fun. Professor Saito can vouch for the science; only you can be the judge of whether we've succeeded on the fun side. I'm not a psychologist myself, but I do understand enough about human nature to know that people don't like long introductions—especially not to a book of games. So I'm going to end by leaving you with a list of eight tips for making your experience with Kokology satisfying, enlightening, and fun.

Enjoy!

—TADAHIKO NAGAO

EIGHT TIPS FOR PLAYING KOKOLOGY

1. Say the first thing that pops into your head.
The games work best when you don't hesitate or agonize over your choice of words. There are no right or wrong answers, so just relax and say whatever springs to mind.

2. Play with other people if you can.
Kokology can be read alone like any other book, but it's most enjoyable, exciting, and entertaining when you play with a partner or in a group. It's a chance to have a few laughs and get to know each other better. You may find that you have more in common than you ever suspected. On the other hand, you may find you're so incompatible that it's as though you're from different planets. There's only one way to find out for sure.

3. Don't try to predict the answers.
It's natural to want to try to outsmart the quizzes or guess what their hidden meanings may be. But what are you going to learn from that?

4. Be honest with yourself.
Kokology may be only a game, but like any good game, it can teach you something about yourself if you let it. Don't be afraid to accept the truth when a minor fault or shortcoming of yours is exposed. I can sense that you're basically a good, intelligent, and likable person. You bought this book, didn't you?

5. Be prepared.

Some of the quizzes will ask you to write something down or draw a picture, so it's a good idea to have a pen or pencil and some paper handy before you start. Advanced-level Kokologists might want to try videotaping a round of games at the next office party. The expressions on people's faces when their true characters are revealed can be priceless. And the secrets they unwittingly blurt out might be worth good money, too.

6. Don't read ahead.

This goes along with the advice of not trying to guess the answers, but it's directed at the group that likes to read the last page of a mystery novel first. Why not open yourself up to a few surprises? Is it really so satisfying to be able to say, "Oh, I knew it all along"?

7. Watch people's reactions (including your own).

The interpretations to the scenarios given in this book are only a starting point for learning more about yourself and others. Sometimes it's more instructive (and entertaining) to see how someone reacts to an answer that's a bit off target than it is to read an interpretation that's right on the money.

8. Keep an open mind.

In Kokology, as in life, it's important to keep things in perspective. There are no correct answers and more than one way of reading any situation. If you're playing with friends, take the opportunity to learn from and about them. What fun would the world be if we all thought alike? Variety is the spice of life.

When Is a Door Not a Door?

I t isn't every day that you have the time to take a leisurely stroll around the neighborhood: a stroll without purpose or destination, a chance to stretch the legs, let the mind wander, and get reacquainted with some old familiar sights. On your way, perhaps you'd stop in at a cozy coffee shop, explore the paths of a favorite park, or take the opportunity to do some window-shopping. Then there are those days when it's enough just to let your feet decide your course. . . .

Picture yourself on a stroll through town. The day is beautiful and you're half-lost in a daydream. You turn onto a street that you've never been down before, and as you walk you pass a beautiful house set somewhat back from the street. Pausing a moment to admire this lovely home, you notice the door is half-open. Why is the door ajar?

1. The house is being burglarized.
2. The owner forgot to close it.
3. The owner is inside, sweeping out the entranceway.

KEY TO "WHEN IS A DOOR NOT A DOOR?"

(D) oors have a twofold significance: they may be passageways, but they can be barriers as well. In particular, the front door of a house represents its first line of defense, all that stands between its inhabitants and the uncertainties of the world outside. By imagining as open a door that should normally be closed, you envision a scenario of vulnerability and exposure. On a subconscious level, the reason you imagined for the door being open is linked to the ways that you leave yourself open and expose your own weaknesses to others.

1. The house is being burglarized.

You instantly assume the worst in any situation, and this trait is nowhere more evident than when things actually do go wrong. You never get flustered in a crisis, but only because you're much too busy panicking. So the next time disaster strikes, it's important to keep a clear head and remember to take a few deep breaths first and count to ten. *Then* you can faint.

2. The owner forgot to close it.

You aren't the type to get carried away in crisis situations. On the contrary, you're so relaxed that you may not notice a crisis is occurring at all. The mistakes you make are caused more by oversight than bad intentions, but the end results for you (and the people around you) are the same.

3. The owner is inside, sweeping out the entranceway.

You may appear to be a laid-back sort, but you never let your guard down. Achieving that constant state of relaxed alertness is what has made you into the mature individual you are. Of course, you still have your human weaknesses; you just don't put them on display for all the world to see.

POSTMARKED: THE FUTURE

L ounging around the house one Saturday afternoon, you are startled out of your reverie by the doorbell. When you open the door, you're greeted by a most unusual surprise—a pair of animal messengers has come to deliver news of your life in the future! But when you open their messages, you see they contain very different predictions of what lies in store for you. One of the animals has brought a letter foretelling a life of happiness and contentment; the other prophesies only disaster and despair.

Which of the animals below brought glad tidings and which an omen of doom? (Pick a different animal for each.)

1. Tiger.
2. Dog.
3. Sheep.
4. Parrot.
5. Tortoise.

KEY TO "POSTMARKED: THE FUTURE"

(F) or most people, the future is greatly influenced by their selection of a mate or life partner. The animal messengers in this scenario actually correspond to your own perceptions of the kinds of people likely to bring you joy and grief. Animals are rich and complex in psychological significance, with a range of positive and negative attributes and associations. In this scenario, the animal you chose as the bearer of the message of happiness represents the type of person you perceive as an ideal spouse, while the doomsayer animal is the type you fear would drag you down into the depths.

1. Tiger.

glad tidings: You see yourself happiest with an ambitious and powerful mate, possessed of an indomitable will to rule.

gloom and doom: You dread the prospect of a vain, tyrannical partner who struts around like a lord of the jungle and growls at any mention of sharing the housework.

2. Dog.

glad tidings: Unquestioning loyalty and absolute devotion are the things you seek most in your mate.

gloom and doom: You are utterly incompatible with those who try to please everyone and fret over what others might be thinking.

3. Sheep.

glad tidings: You see the key to contentment in a warmhearted, nurturing spouse.

gloom and doom: You fear winding up stuck with a boring homebody content to spend each day grazing the same old patch of grass.

4. Parrot.

glad tidings: Nothing would suit you better than a talkative, fun-loving partner who knows how to make you laugh.

gloom and doom: No one could suit you worse than a chattering layabout with a severe allergy to work.

5. Tortoise.

glad tidings: Your match made in heaven is serious, dependable, and sure to be there in your hour of need.

gloom and doom: The prospect of a lifetime spent with a frustratingly slow-moving, slow-witted partner is your worst nightmare.

A Glazed Expression

Arts and crafts class is almost a rite of passage in our society, a grueling test of the human spirit in which young initiates strive to force rubber cement, pipe cleaners, modeling clay, and papier-mâché to bend to their will. And few of us can claim to have managed to avoid the experience of creating an object—be it ceramic mask, napkin holder, or the obligatory ashtray—only to be confronted by an empty expanse demanding that you do something, *anything*, to decorate it.

A plain white coffee mug of your own design sits ready for the kiln and is staring at you in blank anticipation. You have chosen to use blue glaze; now, if only you could decide on the pattern. . . .

Which of the following patterns do you paint in blue on the mug?

1. Stripes.
2. Polka dots.
3. Checks.
4. Wavy lines.

KEY TO "A GLAZED EXPRESSION"

B lue is the color most deeply associated with the inner workings of the mind, from imagination to intuition to intellect. The white surface of your coffee mug provides a blank slate and gives your mind free rein to express itself in the most comfortable, natural way. In this sense, the pattern you selected reflects the structure and strengths of your mind in its approach to creativity and problem solving.

1. Stripes.

You favor a direct and clear-cut approach, making you a keen decision maker able to resolve problems and put plans into action instantly. It's only natural that people perceive you as a leader and pillar of strength in difficult times.

2. Polka dots.

Your strength lies in the adaptive, artistic nature of your mind. This may make you appear to be a little offbeat, perhaps even eccentric to some, but you make a real contribution to the world as a creator with a unique vision.

3. Checks.

You excel at mastering the demands of the everyday, but in no way does that make you average or ordinary. Few people are able to organize their lives with such quiet efficiency. And the result of your efforts is that you always seem to have the time, wealth, and compassion to share with those in need.

4. Wavy lines.

Your gift is in generating an atmosphere in which it's easy and comfortable to feel and express love. It's not that you crave attention or affection, but people just naturally feel good about taking care of and supporting you. And all that goodwill has a ripple effect, touching the lives of those around you in subtle ways. Ask the people who know and love you—the world is a better place for your being in it.

WAVE AFTER WAVE

P erhaps it's because we instinctively trace the roots of life
back to the oceans, perhaps it's something hardwired deep
within our brains; whatever the reason may be, the sea holds a special power over us. The tang of the salt air, the fine spray of the surf,
the soft crashing of the waves—the net effect is to stimulate and
soothe. Sometimes a stroll along a sandy beach can transport you
much further from your everyday reality than the actual distance
you walk. That may be why the sea holds a special place in lovers'
hearts. It provides them with the chance to journey together, if
only for a brief time, into another world.

1. You are walking along a quiet beach. As you wander the dunes,
you spot a surfboard washed up on the sand. Describe the surfboard and the impression it makes on you.

2. You climb onto the board and paddle out to try your luck on the
waves. How are the conditions for surfing today?

3. You have managed to get to your feet and are experiencing the
thrill of actually riding the wave, when suddenly you wipe out and
tumble headfirst into the water. What do you think, feel, or try to
scream as you struggle to find your way back to the surface?

4. You finally emerge from the water unscathed, and looking back toward the beach, you see that a person you know has been watching you. Who is that person?

KEY TO "WAVE AFTER WAVE"

(M) ost of us sense intuitively the strong psychological associations between the sea and sex. The way you imagined your experience on the waves tells us something about your expectations and desires in the sexual realm.

1. Throughout history and across cultures, the sea is portrayed as feminine. Against that backdrop, the surfboard provides an overt example of what Freud referred to as a "phallic symbol." Women: Your description of the surfboard corresponds with your image and impression of masculine sexual characteristics. Men: Your answer shows your perception of your own physical sexuality.

"It's just like every other surfboard out there. You've seen one, you've seen 'em all." Either you haven't seen enough surfboards, or you've seen far too many.

"It's a monster wooden longboard, freshly waxed and gleaming, with a red stripe up the middle." Thanks for sharing, but that's just a little more than any of us wanted to know.

"A sad-looking, beaten-up old board that nobody wants anymore." Don't rush to judgment. Who knows? A little wax, a little buffing, and that old board might look as good as new.

2. The surfing conditions you described reveal your own hopes and expectations from sex.

"The water is warm and inviting. Wave after wave breaks softly on the beach." That's enough to put anyone in the mood.

"The water's a little chilly, and there's not a wave in sight." Don't worry, there will be other days, other chances. Maybe today you can just snuggle up in a beach blanket.

"Towering surf! A fifty-foot tsunami! Cowabunga, baby!!!" Down, boy! Heel!

3. Total submersion within the churning waters is a metaphor for the peak of sexual pleasure. Your thoughts and feelings as you struggled upward correspond to those you experience in the throes of ecstasy.

"Oh, damn—I almost made it that time! I was so close!" I take it you were expecting something more from the experience?

"Help! Somebody please help me! I can't breathe!" Hopefully somebody around here knows mouth-to-mouth.

"Hey, this isn't so bad. I think I'll just stay down here and have a swim around until the wave passes." Don't get too comfortable down there. You're going to have to come up for air *sometime*.

4. The person you pictured standing on the beach is someone you show intense interest in, in a sexual sense. This doesn't necessarily indicate active sexual desire; it may be that you're simply curious

about what that person is like in the most intimate and unguarded of moments. Then again maybe, just maybe, that's something you want to find out firsthand.

Was the person you named your current lover or a secret love interest? That shouldn't be too hard to accept. But then there are always those who name a member of the same sex, a cousin, their dentist. . . . Don't worry, your secrets are safe with us.

BUILDING A NEW TOMORROW

The clock struck twelve, the ball dropped in Times Square, and the sound of champagne corks popping was heard around the globe. And after all the buildup, hoopla, and hype, after the apocalyptic anxieties and eager anticipation, the world somehow managed to find its way safely into the new millennium. Looking back, we can see that the prophecies of doom were overblown and the Y2K bug seems like little more than a ploy to sell system upgrades. But we, the last children of the twentieth century, all shared for a moment that sense of newness and opportunity—the chance to make a world better than the one we inherited and create a legacy to share with our children and theirs over the next thousand years.

1. You are working for an urban planning corporation and have been assigned to the community development team for a major new millennium project. You have been asked to come up with an inspirational theme for the city. What theme do you propose?

2. The project team has a number of members, each with a certain set of experiences and skills. Why do you think you were selected to participate in this project? (Give as many reasons as you like.)

3. What kind of person is the project manager? Describe his or her personality and qualities as a leader.

KEY TO "BUILDING A NEW TOMORROW"

(T) owns and cities are natural symbols of social life. Most of the cities we are familiar with sprang up unplanned and spread outward and upward in a seemingly random fashion. But this scenario asks you to deliberately plan a city for the future, giving your mind the chance to express its vision of an ideal setting for human interaction. Your answers reveal your approach and feelings about the social world around you.

1. The theme you selected for the new city is something you feel is absolutely essential to your own happiness as a member of society. And for most people, that means the very thing they sense is most sorely lacking in their environment at present.

Was your theme something ideal, like "harmony," "peace," or "Mother Nature"? We all feel the need for more of those these days. Or did you pick something along the lines of a cartoon fantasy world where everyone smiles all the time and the sun is always shining? That may actually be an easier goal to achieve, but you're facing some strong competition in Orlando, Anaheim, and Tokyo.

2. The reasons you gave for being picked for the team are strengths you see in yourself that no one else recognizes. That may be because those "strengths" are not quite as strong as you might like to think. The people around you are the most objective judges of

your potential. Don't be afraid to listen to what others have to say about your abilities—their evaluations can steer you away from the dead-end streets of overconfidence and self-deception.

3. The team manager reveals your own image of yourself in the future. Do you see yourself developing into a supportive, motivated, and inspirational leader, or a harsh and unreasonable slave driver? If it's the latter, you may want to start reconsidering the particular path to personal development you're currently heading down. Even Scrooge got the chance to repent.

Dwellers of the Deep

T he undersea world holds mysteries we can barely conceive. Its seemingly endless waters remain the last great frontier on earth, luring adventurers, challenging science, and inspiring poets, artists, and the romantic at heart. The simplest explanation for this allure is that there is more to the ocean than meets the eye. Hidden beneath its featureless surface, millions upon millions of creatures—some familiar, some fantastically strange—live, feed, breed, and die. It is almost as if our planet contained two separate worlds, which have only just begun to discover each other.

Within the box on page 36 is a picture of a coral branch. This exercise requires you to draw an octopus (or more than one) anywhere within the box.

KEY TO "DWELLERS OF THE DEEP"

(C) arl Jung, one of the founders of psychoanalysis, observed that the octopus, with its sinister, alien appearance, slippery invertebrate form, and tentacles that stretch in all directions, is a commonly encountered symbol of stress and anxiety. Your artwork sheds some light on the level and nature of stress in your life.

The size and number of octopuses you drew reflect the importance and number of worries in your life. A single huge octopus indicates a preoccupation with a single great concern, while a number of smaller octopuses swarming everywhere is a sign that you feel overwhelmed by minor stresses and annoyances on all sides. If you drew a small, friendly-looking creature bobbing happily beneath the waves, good for you! No one said that life has to be a cold, dark abyss.

The position of the octopus in relation to the coral is also significant. If you drew a free-floating octopus, it means you believe that your stress, however great it may be, is resolvable. But if you drew the octopus clinging tightly to the coral, it shows you feel as if you're locked in a stranglehold of entanglements.

STAR MATERIAL

Arranging the schedule, approving the wardrobe and makeup, setting up interviews, and handling the fans—the work of a celebrity's personal manager is never done. In this line of business, image is everything. If you want to keep the media buzzing and the lenses of the paparazzi trained, if you want to keep the calls for talk show appearances and concert bookings coming, you need to make sure your client looks the part twenty-four hours a day, every day of the year. The rest of the time, you can relax.

You are the manager of an up-and-coming band. They've got the look, they've got the talent, but for some reason, the records just aren't selling as well as you know they could. Why do you think they haven't been able to make their break into the big time? Give the one reason you see behind their lack of popularity.

Key to "Star Material"

(P) erhaps a manager's most important function is to size up a client's strengths and weaknesses with a cold, objective eye and order the changes that need to be made. By placing yourself in the role of a manager, you took on this same critical perspective. And that piercing gaze quickly located a shortcoming that you have seen but may have been unable consciously to acknowledge in yourself.

Did you say the problem was bad timing, lack of connections, or simply an industry-wide slump in record sales? It's easy to blame all your failings on the outside world, even in your subconscious. Perhaps what you're really trying to say is that your greatest weakness is your inability to accept responsibility and take charge of your destiny.

If the problem was turmoil or infighting among the members of the band, it's likely that you too are plagued by inner conflicts. If you want to be a star, first you're going to have to become your own biggest fan.

If you felt the problem was that the band didn't pay enough attention to their fans, you might want to try taking better care of the people in your life. Remember, it's the people who love you that made you into the star material you are.

HEIGH-HO!

G rumpy, Sneezy, Dopey . . . Doc . . . Happy . . . Sleepy, and . . . what'sisname. Few of us can name all of the seven dwarfs in "Snow White," but the tale just wouldn't be the same without them. After all, they took Snow White in and gave her a place in their home, drove off the evil queen, and kept her lifeless body in safekeeping until she was revived by true love's kiss. We know that Snow White went on to live happily ever after, but whatever became of those seven little fellows?

It is the final scene of "Snow White," and she is riding off into her new life with her handsome prince. You have the power to read the thoughts of the seven dwarfs as they send her off. What are their true feelings at that moment? (It isn't necessary to make your answers conform to the personalities of the dwarfs as they were depicted in the story; just describe seven individual reactions to the scene.)

KEY TO "HEIGH-HO!"

D on't feel Bashful if you couldn't remember the name of that seventh dwarf. Your mind is a very big place, and things are bound to get lost in there from time to time. Most of our minds are so big, in fact, that they play home to a number of entirely different personalities and ways of looking at the world. The ways that you pictured the dwarfs reacting to Snow White's departure illuminate your own true nature and its multiplicity of perspectives.

Did all seven dwarfs wish her well and send her off without hard feelings or regrets? You are decent to the core. If the Magic Mirror judged hearts instead of faces, then *you* would be the fairest one of all.

Or did one or more of the dwarfs mutter something like "That ingrate! After all we did for her! That'll teach me to go out of my way for someone." Too much time in the mines has started to darken your perspective. Maybe you should try whistling while you work.

The amount of diversity in your seven answers also gives an indication of your level of self-integration and internal consistency. If they all ran along the same lines, then, for better or worse, your answers paint an accurate picture of your true character.

If you came up with seven completely different reactions, it could be said that you are capable of entertaining a number of views on any issue. The question you need to ask yourself now is, Which represents the real you?

CAT GOT YOUR TONGUE?

A dog may be man's best friend, but a cat always seems to be its *own* best friend. You may love them or hate them (as if they cared either way), but cats have shared as long a history with us humans as any species of animal on earth, and it's safe to say that they'll be around for ages to come. It's not that cats actually do much for people—they can't fetch the newspaper, shake hands, or play Frisbee—or perhaps it's just that they choose not to. But their cool indifference, quiet pride, and utter impenetrability seem to justify them a place in our world regardless.

We all have our individual perceptions about the cat. Which of the following four phrases strikes closest to the image you hold?

1. Basking in the sun.
2. Mysterious and inscrutable.
3. Pleasantly soft to the touch.
4. A companionless creature.

KEY TO "CAT GOT YOUR TONGUE?"

(I)n Jungian psychology, the cat is a representative of the feminine principle known as the *anima,* or your true inner self (as opposed to the social role you play). The description you selected as applying best to cats reveals the nature of your own true self, in its positive and negative aspects.

1. Basking in the sun.

In describing a catlike activity, rather than the cat itself, you show a sensitivity toward the natural actions of things within their environments. This makes you an accepting and easily acceptable person, capable of getting along well with everyone you meet. On the positive side, this means that people perceive you as comfortable in almost any situation. But that same uncanny sense of comfort can also make you appear to be a little superficial or unconcerned with others.

2. Mysterious and inscrutable.

You instinctively chose to describe the cat in terms of its personality, almost as if it were human. And the attributes of the cat's character that drew your attention are precisely the ones you share with it. Your true inner self is a kaleidoscope, changing and renewing itself constantly. This makes predicting your behavior an endlessly intriguing challenge to the people who love you, but it can also make you seem like more trouble than you're worth to those without the time or inclination to ponder riddles and enigmas.

3. Pleasantly soft to the touch.

To you, the cat presents itself as a physical object, defined specifically in terms of how it affects you. You see the world as something created to stimulate and serve you. This tendency may manifest itself as an aura of calm self-assurance or simply as excessive self-involvement. But it's likely that until you perceive that it has some direct effect on your life, this insight will be of no interest to you either way.

4. A companionless creature.

You define the cat in social terms, showing the emphasis you place on the role of the individual within (or apart from) the group. And your choice of "companionless" to describe the cat's condition is more than a little tinged with feeling, a sense of loneliness that the animal itself does not necessarily share. You are most deeply attuned to the emotional and social realms, making you appear caring, warm, and genuinely concerned about others. But it can also make you seem somewhat overly sensitive and melodramatic when you give full expression to your feelings.

RIDING THE RAILS

most of us approach a ride on the subway with a mixture of fascination and dread. They're crowded, they're noisy, and they aren't famous for their safety or hygiene, but there's something about subways that makes them an integral part of the urban experience. Maybe it's the hum of the electrified rails or the jerky rhythm of sudden starts and stops as the train hurtles from station to station. Or maybe it's their endless ability to surprise even the most hardened city dweller with outrageous shocks and unforeseeable encounters. Whatever it is, subways seem to tempt us with the promise "You thought you'd seen everything? Well, you ain't seen nothing yet."

You're riding on a crowded subway when you see that a single seat has opened up nearby. You are just about to sit down when you notice another person has also begun moving toward the same empty seat. What do you do?

1. Take the seat, of course.
2. Hesitate and look around before doing anything.
3. Let the other person have the seat.
4. Move to another car.

KEY TO "RIDING THE RAILS"

(I) t may not be the most glamorous way to go, and you can't expect much of the view, but sometimes a trip on the subway is the only way to get where you're going. In that sense, subways are a lot like blind dates. And in both situations, it isn't always easy to change course once you've started heading down the wrong track. The way you saw yourself confronting the problem of taking the seat corresponds to the way you would act when you wanted to turn down a second date after a friend had gone to the trouble of introducing you to someone they "just know would be perfect for you."

1. Take the seat, of course.

You know what you want and, just as important, what you don't. Experience has taught you that it makes no sense to agonize over the repercussions for others when it's you who has to live with the consequences. This means you may hurt a few feelings as you go through life, but at least they won't be your own.

2. Hesitate and look around before doing anything.

You always look at the big picture and consider the feelings of everyone involved before making a decision. After all, the world doesn't revolve around you. Just remember, the decision you make now may mean the difference between a comfortable seat and a long ride spent wondering how you ended up on the end of a strap.

3. Let the other person have the seat.

You worry too much about what other people think, and in wanting to look good, you end up acceding to the wishes of others. People praise you as being extremely easy to live with, but if you don't stand up for yourself once in a while, you could be in for a very long trip down a very dark tunnel, stuck with someone who's only too happy to let you stand the whole way.

4. Move to another car.

The very concept of the blind date is alien to you. The prospect of being thrust into a relationship with someone you've never met is enough to make you start reaching for the emergency brake. Fortunately, the people who know you have already figured this out, and despite your many fine qualities, you aren't likely to be at the top of any matchmaker's list of prospects.

THE MIRROR DOESN'T LIE

C lothes shopping provides us with the rare opportunity to confront stark reality in the form of a full-length mirror. We've all been there—the outfit that looked great hanging on the display floor rack undergoes some disturbing metamorphosis on the way back to the fitting room and leaves you standing in clothes that were clearly intended for someone other than you. Then, at that very instant of recognition, the curtain draws back and the sales assistant peeks in to marvel, "Wow, that looks *great* on you!"

How do you respond to this clash of realities?

1. Give a straight account of your opinion: "You've got to be kidding. This looks terrible on me."

2. Point out the specific reasons you don't like the outfit: "The collar is too wide and I don't like the way the sleeves bunch up at the cuffs."

3. Disregard the comment: "Thanks, but I think I'll look around a little bit more."

4. Accept the compliment and say: "Do you really think so? All right, I guess I'll take it."

KEY TO "THE MIRROR DOESN'T LIE"

(S) hopping for new clothes can be likened to a spiritual quest, a time for critical self-assessment as you search for the perfect means to express your true identity. Your wardrobe is an extension of yourself, selected in the hopes of highlighting your best features, physical or otherwise. The way you responded to the clerk's bald-faced flattery reveals the aspect of your self you esteem most dearly.

1. "You've got to be kidding. This looks terrible on me."

Mirrors don't lie, and they have told you that you look good often enough that you can do without empty praise. Your greatest pride is in your appearance, and you aren't about to let some sales clerk in search of a commission spoil the look you've worked so hard to achieve.

2. "The collar is too wide and I don't like the way the sleeves bunch up at the cuffs."

You may not look perfect all the time, but you refuse to be made to look like a fool. You know the power of your mind to perceive the world clearly, and that intellectual pride won't stand being lied to. Your personal style is an expression of refined sensibility and keen powers of discrimination, and you wouldn't dream of compromising that for any reason.

3. "Thanks, but I think I'll look around a little bit more."

Your philosophy is "I'm me, other people are other people," and you never let the two get confused. There is no central source of pride in you, unless it is that you're proud of your unique existence. In the end, you just go your own way and let others think, say, and do as they please.

4. "Do you really think so? All right, I guess I'll take it."

You haven't yet located a source of pride within yourself—if you had, you wouldn't let people manipulate and deceive you like that. It's time you took another honest look in that mirror—you might just be surprised to find that you like what you see. Besides, paying for all those unwanted outfits can get to be a very expensive habit.

READING YOU LIKE A BOOK

You can tell a lot about people from their reading habits. Some are very fussy about their books, refusing to read anything outside of a particular genre or subject matter. Others read indiscriminately, devouring volume after volume without pattern or preference. Many read only on occasion or when work or study demands it. And then there are those who simply don't read at all if they can avoid it.

But for those who do read, not just out of necessity, but for the sheer pleasure and relaxation it affords, finding a good book is almost like making a new friend. There's a sense of simultaneous familiarity and discovery. It's as if a window has opened into a previously unimagined world, but one you sensed was waiting for you all along. Sometimes it's almost as if the book has chosen you.

1. A book lies open in front of you. What type of story does it contain?

2. You begin to read and soon find that you yourself are a character in the story. What kind of role do you play?

3. You read further and come to a section where the pages have been damaged, making them nearly impossible to read. What part of the story is it?

4. You have just closed the cover after finishing the book. How was the ending?

KEY TO "READING YOU LIKE A BOOK"

(W) hile reading habits and preferences may vary widely from person to person, we all share a common experience in which books and reading were an inevitable part of life: our school years. In our culture, books and school are inextricably linked, and the answers you gave in response to this scenario likewise echo your own experiences during school.

1. The type of story you imagined reflects your general impression of your school years.

Does your answer suggest you lived through a comedy, a mystery, or a romance? Then again, who among us didn't?

Or perhaps it was an erotic novel? Either you were a very precocious child or you had an overactive imagination.

A Shakespearean tragedy? The fact that you survived all five acts has added nobility to your character.

2. The role you saw yourself in is the image you have of yourself in your time as a student.

Were you the star of the tale? A sidekick? Comic relief? Or no more than a bit player with only a single line of dialogue on page 283? It may just be that your character was being developed for the sequel.

3. The scene described in the damaged pages mirrors a situation in which you were hurt during your youth. Broken hearts can hurt

as much as an act of violence, and even seemingly minor traumas can take a lifetime to heal. Although at first there might not seem to be any immediate connection to your life, if you think back to your past, it's more than likely you'll find some buried painful memory associated with the scene.

4. The ending of the story is an expression of your feelings of closure (or a lack thereof) regarding your days spent at school.

Did you answer something like "And they rode off into the sunset to live happily ever after"? A little clichéd, perhaps, but you can't argue with success.

Perhaps you envisioned a story in which your character dies in the end? It's likely you greeted your graduation as a chance to be reborn into a new life.

Or was the ending a cliff-hanging "To be continued . . ."? In a way, that's the most accurate response you could give. You'll just have to wait and see how the next episode turns out.

Spill the Wine

An elegant French restaurant: the mood is just right, the maître d' arrived with a fine bottle of red wine, and now, after approving the vintage and performing the obligatory swish test, you are ready to raise your glasses and share a toast between lovers.

But as you lift your glass, your arm jerks and you spill wine on the white tablecloth. From the list below, describe the way the wine spilled.

1. The tablecloth is completely soaked in wine.
2. There are several large red splotches.
3. A few drops of wine spilled out here and there.
4. Fortunately, there's only one small spot on the tablecloth.

KEY TO "SPILL THE WINE"

(W) ine and other alcoholic drinks are associated in the mind with feelings of sexual desire (but not necessarily performance). The way you imagined yourself spilling the wine shows how you perceive your own sexual drive and your ability to keep it under control.

1. The tablecloth is completely soaked in wine.

Your sex drive is operating at 200 percent capacity. We'll let the people who should know best answer as to whether that's a good or a bad thing, but you really should try a little harder to make sure more of that wine of yours reaches its intended target.

2. There are several large red splotches.

Your answer suggests that you feel strong sexual attraction to a number of different people. Attraction is one thing, acting on it is another. Don't let your desire to sample every bottle in the cellar intoxicate you. True connoisseurs have learned to appreciate quality without ever needing to swallow a sip.

3. A few drops of wine spilled out here and there.

You exhibit normal curiosity, but do a good job of reining in your sexual energies, which helps you to avoid trouble and potential embarrassment. If you're quick with your napkin, there's no reason anyone even has to know about those little stains.

4. Fortunately, there's only one small spot on the tablecloth.

Either you have better than average reflexes when it comes to cutting off embarrassing faux pas or there just wasn't much wine in your glass to begin with. Either way, your sex drive is no match for your table manners.

[Your Name Here]

The world is full of other people, and their number grows day by day. For most of us, our social worlds also expand a little each day. Most of our contacts with others are random, chance encounters with people we may never meet a second time. But sometimes fate has other plans, and the stranger you met just yesterday may change your life tomorrow. That uncertainty is one of the things that keep life interesting. Yes, each of our circles of acquaintances is constantly expanding. But when you take a moment to reflect, you may be surprised at how that circle is not as wide as you might have thought.

(For this exercise, you'll need a blank square sheet of paper and a pencil or pen.)

1. First, write your name in a box in the center of the paper.

2. Next, try to fill the remaining blank space on the page with the names of people you know. Take as long as you need, but try to fill in the entire page.

3. Now, draw a single horizontal line through the center of the page. It should cut through the box with your name in it.

4. Finally, choose a name at random in each of the two sections of the page and circle them both.

KEY TO "[YOUR NAME HERE]"

R andomness is a simple and familiar concept, but one the mind has difficulty achieving in practice. Even a conscious and honest attempt to make a random selection is never truly free from the influences of subtle biases and unconscious preferences. The names you picked from the crowded page were determined at least in part by your own perceptions of the people named and how you position them in relation to yourself.

The name you circled in the upper half of the page belongs to someone you respect or see as standing above you. The person whose name you circled in the bottom half is someone you take for granted or look down on. You may be surprised to find that these feelings are in no way related to whether or not you like the people in question. Love and respect do not always go hand in hand.

WHERE THE SKY MEETS THE SEA

There are breathtaking mountain vistas, sweeping metropolitan skylines, rugged tracts of forest that stretch as far as the eye can see, and gentle country landscapes dotted with fields and farms, but of all the scenic views in the world, none can stir the imagination and calm the soul like the unbroken line where the sky meets the sea. That blue horizon is a vast space inviting the mind to relax and unwind, to soar above and dive within, to dream. . . .

You are staying at a resort hotel with an ocean view. Lying on your bed, you gaze out a huge bay window across the cool blue waters, and lulled by the scene, you drift off to sleep. Which of the following views greets you when you awake?

1. A bright midday sun burning over the sea.
2. The dark ocean sleeping beneath a starry night sky.
3. A cool mist rolling in over the waters.
4. The sun just beginning to sink beneath the horizon at dusk.

KEY TO "WHERE THE SKY MEETS THE SEA"

(I) n myths and ancient religions from around the world, the sea and the sky are pictured as an eternal couple, forever holding each other in a loving embrace. The way you envisaged the scene out your hotel room window is your vision of the ideal relationship between two loving partners and shows the things you seek most from love.

1. A bright midday sun burning over the sea.

Passionate excitement and intensity are essential to your ideal romance. For you, love isn't true love if it doesn't burn like a fire, and if that means added danger, it always proves worth the risks in the end.

2. The dark ocean sleeping beneath a starry night sky.

Others may think you're a little hokey or old-fashioned, but you place the greatest emphasis on things like commitment and faithful devotion in a relationship. Your love affairs may not set the sky ablaze, but they will never cause you any sleepless nights, either. And when other loves have clouded over or burst into flames, you will still be enjoying those nights of untroubled sleep—together.

3. A cool mist rolling in over the waters.

The line between friendship and love is blurred for you; the two inevitably flow into each other. Your perfect relationship is with someone you can tell your secrets to, share laughter and tears with, and just relax and be yourself around. You refuse to believe that your lover can't also be your best friend.

4. The sun just beginning to sink beneath the horizon at dusk.

You seek a storybook romance that inspires the world with its picture-postcard perfection. Everything has to be just right, from the meeting, to the first kiss, to the place settings at the wedding, to the house with the white picket fence. True love is a once-in-a-lifetime experience, and you see no reason to settle for less than the very best.

IF THE SHOE FITS

F or many people, finding the right pair of shoes is more than just an excuse to go shopping, it's an obsession. After all, shoes are incredibly important. It's an article of faith to the fashion savvy that footwear puts the finishing touch on every ensemble, and no outfit can survive a poor choice in shoes. And any athlete can tell you that the shoes may not make you run faster, jump higher, or drive the ball farther, but at least you'll look and feel good doing it. And for all of us, there are few better feelings than that first day spent in a pair of comfortable new shoes. Yes, although we may not give them much notice, shoes hold a curious power over our lives.

Imagine that you are a comfortable pair of shoes. If you could pick any person to wear you, who would that person be?

KEY TO "IF THE SHOE FITS"

(W)hen you imagine yourself as another person's shoes, you mentally place yourself in the position where they literally step and walk on you. This image is associated with feelings of self-negation, surrender, and subjection to the will of another.

The person you named as your wearer is someone you can easily imagine yourself utterly enslaved by or would be happy to devote yourself to, body and soul.

Did your response surprise you? Don't be alarmed; there's no shame in wanting to be totally dominated. Well, maybe just a little shame, but that's part of the thrill, isn't it?

SKIMMING THE SURFACE

W e humans excel at many things. However, floating isn't one of them. Sure, with a little practice and a lot of effort we might manage to keep our heads above water for a few laps in the swimming pool, but none of us would fare very well if dropped in the middle of the ocean without a life preserver. But, as always seems to be the case, human ingenuity has made up for the short-comings of the body and provided us with boats. And thanks to those seaworthy craft, now there is no spot on the surface of the world's waters that lies beyond our reach.

Imagine that you are a boat floating on the water. Which of the following best describes you?

1. A raft of rough-hewn logs.
2. A sturdy rowboat.
3. A racing yacht.
4. A cruise ship.

KEY TO "SKIMMING THE SURFACE"

(S) hips and boats are most at home when surrounded on all
sides by nothing but water, unimpeded by obstructions or
boundaries of any kind. Picturing yourself as a boat on the open sea
conjured a similar image of life unfettered by restrictions or limits.
The type of boat you saw yourself as is linked to the ways you prefer
to spend those precious moments when your time is truly your own.

1. A raft of rough-hewn logs.

You spend your free time drifting from place to place and enjoying outdoor activities. Your interests range from intense sports
like kayaking and rock climbing to relaxing pastimes like camping,
fishing, and simply wandering about. The important common
thread is a natural setting, and you might be just as happy to spend
a day lying on your back in the grass, staring up at the clouds.

2. A sturdy rowboat.

Nothing relaxes you like working up a healthy sweat, and it
shows in the ways you spend your days off. High-impact, low-
impact, team sports, or solo, you love the way it feels to put your
body through its paces.

3. A racing yacht.

What better way to spend a lazy summer afternoon than racing
around at breakneck speed? Up-tempo recreations are your pre-

ferred mode of entertainment, whether they take the form of fast-paced sports, high-stakes gambling, or games requiring split-second timing.

4. A cruise ship.

Everyday life is exciting enough as it is, and slow-paced, cerebral activities are just what the doctor ordered when you have time to unwind. A game of chess or a crossword puzzle, a leisurely walk, a nice long book, perhaps a game of shuffleboard—these are the things that you look to when you while away the hours.

MAKE A WISH

Y ou can't have everything. That may seem like a statement of the obvious, but it's surprising how many people seem to forget the fact when making their decisions. Something in human nature refuses to accept that universal rule. We want to believe we can have it all, if only because it makes for a pleasant fantasy. You can dream what you like, but even if you were the wealthiest person on the planet, there would be some things your money couldn't buy. The secret to true contentment lies not in trying to satisfy every craving or desire, but in learning to be satisfied with the things you have. That is a reality of sharing the world with others. But what if it weren't so?

Imagine that you have discovered a magical lamp. A genie appears when you rub it and offers to grant you a single wish in return for setting it free. You can wish for anything in the world you want (with the standard wish granter's stipulation of no wishing for more wishes). What do you wish for?

KEY TO "MAKE A WISH"

(T) he things we wish for are things we think we want most from life, but more specifically, they are things we think we cannot obtain by ourselves. The thing you wished for is something you hope to receive from someone else and corresponds to what you want most from your partner.

Did you ask for fabulous riches or treasure? That wish may someday come true, but many find in acquiring wealth by attaching themselves to another that they are forced to give up something much more valuable than they could ever hope to gain.

Or was your wish for something more intangible, such as limitless power, stunning beauty, or sheer physical pleasure? Reflect on the ways you go about seeking a lover. You may find out too late that pleasure fades, beauty withers, and power corrupts.

Those who wished for wisdom or contentment are already well on the way to finding those wishes come true. The key is only to stop looking for those things to be given you and to discover them within.

DANCING WATERS

Fountains add a touch of magic to any public space. The fine mist carried onto the breeze, the gentle sounds of water falling into water, the sparkle of light as it plays on the rippling surface: it's enough to transform a humdrum little park into a fantasy setting. Perhaps that's why the local fountain is such a popular meeting place for romantic assignations and getting together with friends.

Close your eyes and imagine a park with a fountain. You have arranged to meet some friends there before a night out on the town. What kind of fountain do you see?

1. A single jet of water blasting straight up in the air like a geyser.
2. A number of medium-size fountains in a sparkling array, their spray dissolving into droplets of mist.
3. A smallish, burbling fountain.
4. An intricately engineered and complex water sculpture.

KEY TO "DANCING WATERS"

(T) hey may be impressive, enchanting, even magical. They may inspire romance or sheer awe. But one thing you can't say about fountains is that they're practical. The water goes up, the water comes down—what does it achieve? Nonetheless, we sense that the world would be a poorer place without them. Sometimes you need to forget about practicality and just cut loose and enjoy. And therein lies the key to this scenario: The type of fountain you imagined is related to the way you spend your money when enjoying a night out with friends.

1. A single jet of water blasting straight up in the air like a geyser.

You're like a magician with money, able to make vast quantities disappear in the blink of an eye. It doesn't matter much to you the way that you consume it, just as long as you don't leave any leftovers. This makes you everybody's friend the first weekend after payday and explains why people around the office have taken to calling you "Old Faithful."

2. A number of medium-size fountains in a sparkling array, their spray dissolving into droplets of mist.

You like to use money to impress, spending it in a flashy way to guarantee maximum effect. You have been known to order food you don't even like, simply because it was the most expensive thing on the menu. As long as you're willing to keep paying the tab, there will always be people willing to act impressed.

3. A smallish, burbling fountain.

You are a conservative spender—that is, on those rare occasions when you spend anything at all. You figure the sales tax for everyone's bill when you split the tab and *then* whip out your coupons. Your spending habits definitely aren't going to make you go broke, but if you don't loosen up those purse strings a little, you may find yourself going solo.

4. An intricately engineered and complex water sculpture.

You're a schemer, always trying to make more out of your money than was there to begin with. You count convincing a waitress that you qualified for the kiddie meal discount when you were fifteen as one of your proudest accomplishments. It's not the money itself that's at issue, it's just a medium you use to express your creative impulses. That may earn you a bright future in trading stock options, but getting thrown out of a movie theater for sneaking in the emergency exit is not a good way to score points on a date.

HAPPY LANDINGS

Every day, people pay good money for the privilege of stepping out the door of a moving airplane and plunging to earth. Skydiving isn't for everyone, but the statistics tell us it's actually a low-risk venture, considerably safer than, say, trying to cross against the light in Manhattan traffic. But even knowing that, we have a hard time finding a rational explanation for the act. Some say it's the adrenaline, but for veteran enthusiasts, that purely physical rush has worn off after the first few jumps. The thing that really keeps calling them back is those brief few minutes of perfect clarity as the natural world lies spread out in miniature beneath their feet, with everything put into proper perspective. Yes, the old-timers will tell you, it's not the thrill of the jump, it's the view on the way down.

You are in mid-descent, floating slowly earthward under the canopy of your open parachute. Describe the view as you look down.

1. A field of grass and flowers.
2. A craggy, rocky landscape.
3. Wild animals waiting with open jaws.
4. A flowing river.

KEY TO "HAPPY LANDINGS"

(T) hey say that the fall doesn't kill you, just the landing. And the image of the landing that awaits you shows your general attitude and expectations about what the world holds in store for you. The scene you selected reveals your level of optimism or pessimism toward life.

1. A field of grass and flowers.

You are the eternal optimist. You can probably smell the flowers from eight thousand feet and were pleased to note that the grass was growing especially thick to cushion your fall. At this altitude, life is beautiful; just don't get so engrossed in the view that you forget to tuck and roll.

2. A craggy, rocky landscape.

You think Murphy was an optimist: when nothing can go wrong, it will anyway. Well, at least your chute hasn't gotten tangled. Yet. You should try looking more on the bright side of things. After all, right now you're on top of the world. The only place to go is . . . down.

3. Wild animals waiting with open jaws.

You don't mind that the world is out to get you, but only because it's so fun to watch. You view your fate with a kind of resigned bemusement and never pass up the chance for a laugh, even when it's at your own expense.

4. A flowing river.

You are neither pessimist nor optimist, but take things as they come and deal with problems as they arise. You recognize that no one knows enough about the future to decide whether it will be "good" or "bad," and besides, you've got enough things to concern yourself with right here in the present. Specifically, like whether or not to aim for the riverbank to reduce the risk of drowning or angle toward the deepest part to soften the crunch of impact.

WHO'S TO BLAME?

T ake a moment to reflect on your romantic history. How many times have you said, "This is it. I've finally found my one true love"? And how many times has the reality turned out differently? Paperback romances and fairy tales promote an ideal of a first and only love, but few of us can claim to have had such uncomplicated good fortune. For most people, the process of finding the perfect partner is one of trial and error: breakups, makeups, missed opportunities, and misunderstandings. Human love is a fragile creation, and sometimes the smallest thing—the wrong choice of words or a single clumsy gesture—can make love shatter, stall, or fade away.

Think of the last three people you have loved in your life, and write down the reasons each of those relationships ended (or failed to begin). Try to be as specific as possible in giving the reasons. For example, in a case of unrequited love, state whether it didn't work out because the other person didn't notice your signals or just wasn't interested, or whether it was because you lacked the courage to say how you felt. In completing this exercise, avoid vague, noncommittal statements like "It just wasn't meant to be," "It wasn't really anybody's fault," or "We were both a little bit at fault." Take as long as you need to answer, but assign the blame to one side or the other in each case.

KEY TO "WHO'S TO BLAME?"

B eing the judge in the court of love is not always easy. Were you able to render a final verdict in each case before you? Some people can dash off a list of reasons as fast as they can write. Others take much longer to deliberate before arriving at a decision.

The key to this exercise is not an analysis of the content of your responses, but the time you spent deciding on them. The amount of time it took you to assign and accept blame reveals your attitude toward and aptitude for romantic love.

By definition, breakups and rejections are negative experiences. People who are able to produce reasons without much hesitation are focused too intently on the negative aspects of their love lives. They may be rich in experience but have yet to derive any real benefit from it. If you fall in this category, you need to concentrate more on the positive side of things before you can hope to attain or inspire happiness in love.

The inability to assign blame quickly actually reveals a tendency to remember the good and forget the bad, which is an important ingredient in the recipe for success in love relationships. You may have hurt others, or been hurt yourself, but on the whole you see your romantic past as a series of positive learning experiences. For you love is, as it should be, an enjoyable opportunity for growth.

A Perfect Ten

Looks: 10
Brains: 10
Personality: 10

F ew people get the chance to meet someone who matches that description, but it's nice to believe that somewhere out there, there's a perfect ten. Someone who makes the sun shine a little brighter just by getting out of bed in the morning. Someone it would be an honor just to be in the same room with. But how would you approach such a charmed individual? What could you possibly talk about? The prospect of encountering true perfection is a little intimidating, but in the end, wouldn't it be enough just to stand back and admire the view?

Picture in your mind the ideal woman: strong and gentle, graceful and wise, beautiful in every sense. Which of the situations below best fits your image of her?

1. She is exploring the streets of some exotic locale.
2. She is engaged in a romance with an equally ideal lover.
3. She is standing on a stage, basking in the spotlight as the crowd calls out for more.
4. She is behind the wheel of a high-performance sports car.

KEY TO "A PERFECT TEN"

$\left(\text{I}\right)$ t may be because we all carry some idealized image of our mothers from infancy, or it may be that women are just naturally closer to perfection than members of certain other genders. Whatever the case, it is a fact that people tend to find it easier to imagine a perfect woman than a perfect man. In envisioning this ideal person, you opened your mind to your own potential for perfection. The setting you selected was the one that you felt was best suited to a perfectly fulfilled individual and corresponds to what you see as the nearest route to achieving your own self-realization.

1. She is exploring the streets of some exotic locale.

You associate human perfection with situations where mood and the ability to stir the emotions play a primary role. You place similar emphasis on the feeling side of your nature, and the road to self-realization is leading you to a career as an artist or creator. Let your dreams be your road map, and they'll never lead you astray.

2. She is engaged in a romance with an equally ideal lover.

Your preferred sphere of activity is the world of human relationships. All of our paths through life intersect with the paths of many others, and your success in particular will be determined by your strength at forming partnerships, forging alliances, and building networks of personal connections.

3. She is standing on a stage, basking in the spotlight as the crowd calls out for more.

You are at your best in situations that allow you to exercise your personal magnetism and charismatic charm over a group. You have the power to fascinate and inspire, and even if you choose not to play the part of a star, someday you may find that role is thrust upon you.

4. She is behind the wheel of a high-performance sports car.

You demand control over your destiny and can't be satisfied with sitting still. These qualities are what make you so impeccably suited to the role of leader. You may have to take the first step by declaring your independence and striking off on your own, but rest assured, one day you will be the one making the decisions and giving the orders.

SNIP

H and most people a pen and paper and ask them to draw something specific, and they will draw it for you without a second thought. But give them the same pen and paper and ask them to draw anything they like, and most will freeze up for a moment. Sometimes the prospect of total freedom makes us hesitate more than the most challenging obstacle.

You have a single sheet of paper and a pair of scissors. You've been asked to cut the paper into two halves in any way you like. How do you cut the paper?

1. A clean cut straight down the middle.
2. A line curving back and forth several times.
3. A jagged-edged cut.
4. A single gently rounded curve.

KEY TO "SNIP"

$\left(\text{C}\right)$ utting off a relationship is much like cutting a page in two. There's no reason either of the processes needs to be complicated—a few quick snips and you're done. But things don't always work out so easily in real life. It could be simple clumsiness born of haste, but often there's more to it than that. Sometimes making a clean cut just doesn't seem to suit the situation. Sometimes we like to get creative, to express the way we really feel.

1. A clean cut straight down the middle.

When you end a relationship, you really end it, without hand wringing, regrets, or remorse. This stems from your belief that clean cuts are the most painless and heal without leaving scars, a surgical principle you apply with cold, objective precision in all realms of your life. As a result of that "right down the middle" approach, you have probably managed to accumulate a few half sets of cutlery, some mateless chairs, and an encyclopedia that only goes up to M.

2. A line curving back and forth several times.

You agonize over your decisions, fretting endlessly over how to ensure that no one is left feeling angry or hurt. But playing the waiting game only prolongs the agony for you and everyone involved. Sometimes you vacillate so much that it makes your head spin. Breakups are hard enough as it is, there's no reason they have to make you seasick, too.

3. A jagged-edged cut.

Maybe "Rip that damn paper into tiny pieces" is a better way to describe how you exit a relationship. You don't burn your bridges—you blow them up. To your way of thinking, the phrase *happy ending* is an oxymoron. And in the spirit of fairness, you try to make sure that everybody gets their share of the grief.

4. A single gently rounded curve.

The hopeless romantic in you prefers "au revoir" to "adieu," and you never see the logic in breaking up when it's obvious that all you both need is to spend some time apart. But don't forget that not everyone shares your undying sense of optimism. Sometimes "It's over—I never want to see you again" means just that.

WHEN THE PARTY'S OVER

Y ou drew the short straw and ended up with the unenviable task of being designated driver for the night. You resign yourself to a long night of club soda and cocktail nuts and manage to make it all the way to the agreed-upon twelve o'clock final round. But your jolly companions have different ideas, and with eyes out of focus and beer on their breath, the call goes out for "Just one more for the road!"

Nobody likes to be a wet blanket, but you've had enough. What do you say to convince your drunken friends that it really is time to go home?

1. "If you stay out any later, there's going to be hell to pay when you get home."

2. "If I don't get home soon, I'm going to have to sleep in the dog-house."

3. "You've had enough already. Let's go before you make yourself sick."

4. "Come on, party's over. I've got to get up early tomorrow."

KEY TO "WHEN THE PARTY'S OVER"

(T)here's a reason they call it "baby-sitting a drunk." Drunks are like children in many ways: they laugh and cry at the silliest things; they have difficulty finishing their sentences; sometimes they even wet their pants. But the most relevant similarity in this scenario is that both can be a nightmare to control for the people who are supposed to be responsible for them. The way you tried persuading your partying friends to call it a night tells us something about your current (or future) parenting style.

1. "If you stay out any later, there's going to be hell to pay when you get home."

You don't want your children to think of you as an ogre, but sometimes the coercive power of a believable threat is too much to resist. That's the nice thing about having a partner. You can scare the kids into behaving with, "Just wait till Dad gets home!" or, "Mom is going to freak when she sees this mess," and still come away looking like the nice half of the good cop/bad cop routine. But you can't always be your kids' best friend. Sometimes you have to settle for being their parent.

2. "If I don't get home soon, I'm going to have to sleep in the doghouse."

You take the "best pals" strategy (see #1, above) to the next step, asking your kids to protect you from the consequences of their misbehavior. But in this approach, not only do you turn your spouse into the bad guy, but by abdicating all responsibility, you relinquish your own authority as well. It may be time for a refresher course in Parenting 101.

3. "You've had enough already. Let's go before you make yourself sick."

Your no-nonsense, "stick to the facts" approach may not win you any nominations in the "Coolest Parent Ever" awards, but you always have your kids' best interests at heart. And in the long run, that more than anything else will earn you their love and respect.

4. "Come on, party's over. I've got to get up early tomorrow."

You have a tendency to put your own priorities ahead of those of your kids. Parenting involves self-sacrifice, and that isn't always easy to do. But once you've drawn that straw, it's a reality you're going to have to come to terms with. Who knows, you may even learn to love it.

A LITTLE HORSE SENSE

W atching a trained horse and rider, you can easily get the impression that the two have somehow been fused into one. Learning to ride a horse is not an easy thing to do, but for those who have mastered the equestrian art, the experience is its own reward. There's a thrill in having a powerful steed respond instantly to your every command, and the finest riders admit that when they're in the saddle it's almost as if the horse has become an extension of their own bodies.

If you were a rider in a horse show and could select your mount, what kind of horse would you choose to be seen on?

1. A graceful steed with muscles rippling beneath its shining coat.
2. A Thoroughbred of unquestionable lineage.
3. A lovable companion with a sensitive, knowing gleam in its eye.
4. A one-in-a-million horse that's not only intelligent, but beautiful as well.

KEY TO "A LITTLE HORSE SENSE"

(A) horse is a horse, of course, of course—unless, of course, it's a subconscious representation of your own sexual self-image. In choosing the horse you wanted to be seen on, you based your selection on the things you most want potential lovers to notice in you. The type of horse you picked corresponds to what you see as your own strongest sales point in attracting members of the opposite sex. Of course, how the rest of the world sees things is sometimes another matter entirely.

1. A graceful steed with muscles rippling beneath its shining coat.

You are most confident in your own appearance: beautiful skin, great body, perfect hair. You know you look good, and you feel good about it. That confidence may even be borne out by the facts, but whether it is or not, you should realize that the best riders choose their mounts for qualities other than just the way they look on the show grounds. Come race time, you're still going to be expected to perform.

2. A Thoroughbred of unquestionable lineage.

Sophistication and good breeding are what distinguish you from the crowd. Or so you believe. But what you see as marks of an elite background may actually make you seem just a little spoiled or full of yourself. True breeding is reflected in character. And that's something you'll have to let the rest of the world find in you for itself.

3. A lovable companion with a sensitive, knowing gleam in its eye.

You want to be known for your sense of humor, sparkling conversation, and lively wit. There's no doubt that you're good at engaging in banter and making small talk. But remember—sometimes jokes build bridges, and sometimes they build walls. It might be wise to take a look around you from time to time and see if you're the only one who's laughing.

4. A one-in-a-million horse that's not only intelligent, but beautiful as well.

Whatever your weak points may be, lack of confidence isn't one of them. You may in fact be beautiful and smart. You might even be charming, funny, and athletic to boot. But that high assessment of yourself can also serve to put distance between you and the rest of us mere mortals. Don't try so hard to impress people. You don't need to prove anything. After all, if not for that overconfidence, you might just be perfect.

Sweets for the Sweet

We've all heard the story of the little girl and boy lost in the woods who stumble upon a house made of tempting sweets. And even when we know that it's a trap laid by a cunning witch, it's hard not to sympathize with those hungry children as they begin to pick away at the cookie doorknobs, candy glass windowpanes, and sugar-frosted roof shingles. After all, what child (or adult, for that matter) could be expected to resist such a treat?

Imagine you are lost in a dark forest and starting to feel the first pangs of hunger when you come across a cottage made of sweets. After checking the area to make sure no witches are lurking about, you get ready to dig in. How do you set about consuming the house?

1. I'd just start eating everything in sight.
2. I'd try sampling as many different kinds of sweets as I could find.
3. I'd find my one favorite sweet and stick to that.
4. I'm not very into sweets. Actually, I'd prefer some crunchy mixed nuts.

KEY TO "SWEETS FOR THE SWEET"

(C) andy and snacks are not something you give much thought to in preparing, or eat only at set mealtimes. Most of the time, it seems they just end up in your stomach without your knowing how they got there. Personal relationships have a similar way of forming without conscious planning or deliberation. But that's not to say that subconscious preferences don't play a role. On a behavioral level, the way you approached the candy cottage mirrors your approach to the world of friendships.

1. I'd just start eating everything in sight.

You are always up front and out in the open in dealing with the world, almost like a child in your innocent enthusiasm. This straightforward approach makes you easy for others to understand and accept, but you should realize that not everyone is as forth-right and honest as you. Sometimes that honesty of yours makes you just a little too trusting, and you have been known to rush in where angels wouldn't dare to tread.

2. I'd try sampling as many different kinds of sweets as I could find.

The world is full of people, and you wouldn't mind the chance to meet them all. You are a true master at finding the good quali-ties in others. But your desire to have a little taste of everything can also be read as an unwillingness to get too deeply involved with any one person. While it's good to be able to enjoy all kinds of tastes, there comes a time when you're going to have to finally admit to someone, "You're the sweetest of them all."

3. I'd find my one favorite sweet and stick to that.

If you can find even a single person in the world who shares your interests, tastes, and aspirations, that's enough for you. It is indeed a wonderful thing to be able to find a person who sees the world exactly as you do, but by limiting yourself to a single flavor of relationship, you may be cutting yourself off from a whole world of delicious experiences.

4. I'm not very into sweets. Actually, I'd prefer some crunchy mixed nuts.

For you, the word *crazy* has a positive connotation. Accordingly, your circle of friends and acquaintances has more than the average number of interesting characters. The life of an outsider has its appeal, and you enjoy the perspective that taking a step back from the crowd affords you. But in trying to set yourself apart, you may sometimes be seen as someone who's trying too hard to be different. It's important to remember that the people who are most afraid of being thought ordinary are those to whom that description best applies.

ALL HEAVEN'S CHILDREN

T here are some things that are difficult to accept outright, but which we want to believe in nonetheless. Kindly fairies, mysterious ghosts, Santa Claus. The concept of heavenly angels in particular seems to capture the imagination, and few people are willing to deny the possibility that they exist. It's comforting to think of them looking down upon us with goodwill and compassion, ready to aid us in our darkest hour of need. And what harm could possibly come from having a little faith in divine providence?

Imagine that you are an angel, pictured in the box on page 95. As you soar through the heavens, you hear a fallen angel (or several) calling out to you. How many angels do you see, and what are they saying to you? Draw a picture of the angel(s) and write their words in the empty space in the box.

KEY TO "ALL HEAVEN'S CHILDREN"

I n depth psychology, the fallen angel is a symbol of same-sex love. All people pass through a stage in which they are most actively interested in members of the same gender. This interest is not limited to homosexuality, but also forms the basis for strong loving friendships and other platonic relations. It is normal to be attracted in some way or another to people of your own gender. Your responses to this exercise show just how deep and strong those attractions are in you.

The size and number of the fallen angels you drew is a gauge of your level of attraction to members of the same sex. The greater the size and number, the stronger your interest, latent or otherwise. The positions of the angels in relation to the picture of your angel also show the strength of the attraction. If you drew a crowd of angels surrounding you, or one close enough to touch, you may feel as if you are struggling with temptation on all sides, or that the object of your desire is tantalizingly within your reach.

The words of the angels calling out to you are an expression of the voice of your own subconscious. If they taunted you with cries of "Why don't you come and join us? You're missing out on the real fun down here!" or "Don't be so high and mighty. This could be you someday," it indicates a certain curiosity (or at least a willingness to hear more) about alternates to the orthodox paradise. But if the angels only rejected you—"We don't need your kind around here. Fly back up to heaven where you belong!"—then it's likely you feel little in the way of subconscious desire toward members of your own sex.

If this quiz reveals some unexpected leanings in you or your partner (or both!), we'll let you work that out between yourselves. Just remember, heaven smiles on all forms of love.

TIME FOR A CHANGE

Y ou don't need an interior decorator or feng shui adviser to tell you that sometimes the smallest changes to a room's decor can have a surprisingly large impact. You don't have to replace or rearrange the furniture; merely applying a different color of cushions on the sofa, adding a new floor plant or a print on the wall, or even switching from bright white to soft yellow lightbulbs can utterly transform the way a familiar room feels. Sometimes all it really takes is a good session with the vacuum and a feather duster. Whatever the changes, big or small, they're sure to make you see your home in a new light.

You have decided to buy a new tablecloth for your dining room table. What kind of tablecloth do you want?

1. A simple white tablecloth.
2. A tablecloth in a "warm" color, such as fuchsia, mustard, or apricot.
3. A tablecloth in a "cool" color, like periwinkle, teal, or moss.
4. A tablecloth with a bright, multicolored pattern.

KEY TO "TIME FOR A CHANGE"

(W) e're all decorators within, letting our hearts decide the way we want our surroundings to look. The dining room is a center of home life, and the table represents the stage across which many family dramas play out. Perhaps without realizing it, you chose the tablecloth you did for more than just the way it fit the color scheme. Your choice also reveals the atmosphere you want to create, or the thing you place most importance on, in your family life.

1. A simple white tablecloth.

Whether it's a father who's always shouting to keep the volume down, an ongoing marital dispute over bathroom rights, or just the feeling of being hemmed in by the endless responsibilities of raising a family in a busy world, the things you sense your home lacks most are personal space and freedom. That white tablecloth might help a little, but for real elbow room there's nothing quite like a move to a bigger house.

2. A tablecloth in a "warm" color, such as fuchsia, mustard, or apricot.

Your home suffers most from a lack of open lines of communication. You may have noticed that family meals are declining in frequency, and even when you do manage to get everyone together, it can be hard to get a discussion going. The condition is serious, but not irreversible. As you intuitively sensed, if you make your home a warm and comfortable place to be together, those family conversations will start to flow naturally again.

3. A tablecloth in a "cool" color, like periwinkle, teal, or moss.

You have a close family, sometimes a little too close for comfort. People can't seem to get out of each other's way in your home, and it always seems as if somebody's toes are getting stepped on. It's admirable that your family is so tightly knit; now, if you could only find a way to turn down the tension level a notch. . . . If that tablecloth doesn't work, a little Mantovani in the background during dinner might just do the trick.

4. A tablecloth with a bright, multicolored pattern.

The environment in your home is sedate. Sometimes you think "comatose" might be a better description. It feels as if your home has become no more than a place to collapse after another long day, and perhaps a little colorful enhancement would provide a much needed shot of vitality. It takes only one person to strike the match that gets the home fire burning again. Maybe that someone could be you.

A DAY TO REMEMBER

T he flowers you wore to the prom are faded and brittle, an uncomfortable number of the faces in the yearbook look unfamiliar, and most of the things you learned in trigonometry seemed to vanish from your memory the instant you handed in the final to be graded. But some memories from high school stay fresh in everyone's minds, always readily available whenever the urge for a trip down memory lane should strike.

Think back to your high school graduation ceremony. Which of the following images stands out most clearly in your mind?

1. The face of the principal handing out diplomas and shaking hands.
2. The banner reading "Congratulations to the Class of XXXX."
3. The ranks of students standing proudly in their caps and gowns.
4. The playing of the graduation march.

KEY TO "A DAY TO REMEMBER"

$\left(G\right)$ raduation ceremonies follow certain fixed patterns, but ask ten different people to describe their impressions, and it's probable that they'll describe ten very different scenes. People naturally tend to focus on different aspects of the world and therefore find certain types of information easier to recall than others. The thing you remember most clearly about your graduation shows the area where your powers of recall are strongest.

1. The face of the principal handing out diplomas and shaking hands.

You have a special aptitude for remembering faces and names. Meet someone once, and you never need to be introduced again. And that is a skill that has stood you in good stead on more than one occasion, making people you barely know feel like valued friends.

2. The banner reading "Congratulations to the Class of XXXX."

You've got a strong head for figures—birthdays, telephone numbers, batting averages, the number of steps from your front door to the car. You might not remember the name of someone you ate lunch with last week, but you could probably recollect how much you paid for the meal. Those powers of recall have earned you a reputation as serious and dependable. After all, you never forget a date.

3. The ranks of students standing proudly in their caps and gowns.

You don't remember things so much as you reminisce about them. Your ability to recall a scene is inextricably tied to the emotions it aroused in you, and you can almost experience the feelings again just by turning your mind's eye that way. This allows you to replay and enjoy happy memories over and over again. But it also means you have difficulty forgiving and forgetting after you've been hurt.

4. The playing of the graduation march.

Visual memories seem to fade quickly for you, but the things you hear and say are stored in a permanent file that you can access as easily as pulling a CD from the shelf. When your memory of an event is blurred, sometimes all it takes is hearing a snatch of a melody that was playing in the background at the time to cause the memories to come flooding back to you.

Winning Isn't Everything

T eam sports generate as much passion in the stands as they do on the field, and the excitement surrounding a football championship, World Cup soccer match, or final-round basketball playoff is intense enough to send waves of energy around the world. In fact, it's often the case that the fans get more carried away by the action than do the players themselves.

1. You are in the stands at a championship sporting event and the team you are cheering for is defending against a critical drive toward the goal as the final seconds of the game tick away. What do you shout to the players on your team?

2. Your favorite player commits a flagrant violation and is ejected from the game, but only after protesting violently. Describe the referee's demeanor as he sends your unruly hero to the sidelines.

3. Three . . . two . . . one . . . the timer counts down to zero and your team has suffered a disastrous loss. Describe your honest response to this setback.

KEY TO "WINNING ISN'T EVERYTHING"

(T) eam sports are a form of cultural ritual in which the human needs for aggression and conflict are channeled toward a more positive end. Positive as long as your team wins, that is. The way you reacted to your team's performance reveals how you respond to interpersonal confrontations, particularly those you get the worst of.

1. The way you cheered (or jeered) your squad is an indication of how you react when engaged in a heated debate or difference of opinion. Did you offer unconditional support, cheering, "Go team, go"? Right or wrong, you're not the type to go down without a fight.

Or did you engage in some criticism from the safety of the bleachers—"What are those bums thinking? My grandmother could play better!" That lack of a loyal fan base may itself be the biggest hole in your defense.

2. The ref's reaction to the foul parallels your own expression when you are in a confrontation with another person. Did he maintain an unruffled, professional demeanor, or did he get carried away in the heat of the moment? As much as we'd like to see refs keep their cool, the men in stripes are only human.

3. Your response to your team's defeat shows how you might respond when you come out on the losing end of an argument.

"You can't win 'em all. We'll get 'em next time!" You may not be cut out for competitive sports—or the debate team—but there's definitely a place for you on the pep squad.

"I've had it with those losers. I'm never cheering for them again." But if you don't cheer for them, who will?

REAL FEAR

T he experience of virtual reality has been around for much longer than most people think—we call it a trip to the movies. A good film draws you into another world, playing out larger than life on a panoramic canvas and leaving only a pair of eyes there in the darkened theater to follow the action on-screen. And of all the emotions a movie can evoke, none can grip an audience so completely as fear. There is no such thing as virtual fear. Your heart pounds, your breath comes fast and shallow, your nerves are like live wires, and your stomach rises into your throat. If that isn't real, nothing is.

Everyone enjoys a good scare once in a while. Which of the following thrillers scares the pants off you?

1. A vengeance-crazed woman hunting down and destroying the people she hates.
2. A big-budget disaster flick with passengers trapped belowdecks aboard a sinking ocean liner.
3. A sinister serial killer selecting his victims at random.
4. An unstoppable alien life form wreaking havoc on earth.

KEY TO "REAL FEAR"

W e watch thrillers, chillers, slashers, and shockers because we want to be scared in a safe way. But it isn't necessary to go to a theater or video store to experience fear; the real world is frightening enough as it is. When selecting a scary movie, we don't just want to be scared; we choose to be scared by exactly those things that scare us most. The type of film you selected reveals a source of anxiety that doesn't disappear from your mind after the ending credits roll.

1. A vengeance-crazed woman hunting down and destroying the people she hates.

Inhabiting a world filled with billions of other people scares you silly. The realm of personal relationships is a snakepit of unpredictable reactions and irrational acts. Perhaps you've already been involved in a few horror stories starring friends, family, or lovers, but sometimes you just wish the world would leave you alone and go scare somebody else.

2. A big-budget disaster flick with passengers trapped belowdecks aboard a sinking ocean liner.

You're sensitive to the plight of the passengers plunged from the heights of luxury to the depths of despair because you fear nothing more than an assault on the positive image you have of your life. You want to believe that things can be perfect, and you go out of your way to avoid any suggestion to the contrary. But just as no ship is unsinkable, there's no such thing as a perfect life. But don't let that bother you too much; on that score we're all in the same boat.

3. A sinister serial killer selecting his victims at random.

You seek safety in numbers against an incomprehensible, sometimes hostile world. You fear being separated from the group, where you might make easy prey, and this means you're sometimes too willing to sacrifice your identity in order to fit in. But the only way to make true friends—the kind who will stand by you when danger looms—is to have the courage to be yourself.

4. An unstoppable alien life form wreaking havoc on earth.

You fear that you're being overrated by the people around you, people you see as depending on you to be strong. You don't want to let those people down, but you're afraid that someday there will be a crisis too big for you to handle. Relax, you don't have to be perfect. Accept yourself and your limitations. No one else expects you to be invincible—why should you?

MUSIC BOX

Music boxes are designed for the sole purpose of making people feel good. They call us back to simpler times, lull us to sleep with their delicate tunes, even make us feel young again. All it takes is a few turns of the key. But behind that simple purpose lies a complex mechanism of interlocking cogs, gears, and wheels. Every chime a hammer strikes is also a signal that the tune is winding down toward its end.

You fell in love with a particular music box at an antiques store, bought it on impulse, and took it home. Its melody is beautiful, but one day it suddenly stops playing.

1. How long after you bought the music box did it cease to play?
2. What do you think as you hold the broken music box in your hands?

KEY TO "MUSIC BOX"

(T) he music box is a symbol of beauty and pleasure that is fated to come to an end. But it also represents the repetition of the same old tune over and over again. The way you perceived your antique music box shows some of your expectations from the pleasures of romance and the sense of how it may one day end.

1. The amount of time you thought the music box continued to play corresponds to your expectations of how long love will endure.

Years? A few months? Two or three days? That's such a shame. After all, it takes only a little tender loving care and the music should play forever.

2. The way you felt about the broken music box shows how you feel when a relationship has died.

Did you shrug it off as inevitable and toss it in the trash? Mutter something about the poor quality of the workmanship and curse yourself for wasting your money? Maybe you resolved to go out shopping for a new one right away?

Or did you try to think of a way to get it working again? Sometimes all it takes is one good whack in the right spot.

SOME ROOM FOR IMPROVEMENT

Good real estate brokers understand that whether it's a one-room studio apartment or a three-bedroom Cape Cod with a yard, their clients are looking for more than four walls and a door. They're looking for a place to call home. Model showrooms are designed with that in mind. The interior design and furniture are carefully selected to create a feeling in potential home buyers: "This is where I want to be. This is where I belong."

You have recently been to see a model home and are now mulling over whether or not to sign the lease. The tour was unhurried, and you had the chance to ask the questions you had prepared, but there's one part of the home that you still want to spend a little more time looking over before you can feel comfortable in making your final decision.

Which area do you want to examine again?

1. The bathroom.
2. The bedroom.
3. The dining room/kitchen.
4. The veranda/garden.

KEY TO "SOME ROOM FOR IMPROVEMENT"

I n psychoanalysis, houses are commonly encountered representations of the body, and the search for a new home corresponds to the quest for physical self-improvement. Accordingly, the area of the home that you expressed the most interest in is related to the ways that you seek to improve your own body. More specifically, the space in the home that you were not completely satisfied with shows what factors tend to stand in the way of your diet, exercise, or self-renewal plans.

1. The bathroom.

The bathroom is the place where the body is cleansed and represents the urge toward renewal and purging of the self. You who chose the bathroom as the source of dissatisfaction intuitively sense that your own commitment to a better self may not be strong enough.

2. The bedroom.

Bedrooms are cognitively associated with the desire for physical relaxation and comfort. You who wanted to see more of the bedroom actually wanted to see more of the bed; to kick off your shoes and snuggle under the covers. Your problem isn't with the idea of diets or physical exercise, just with all the work that's involved.

3. The dining room/kitchen.

These rooms have strong associations with the desire for food, and food itself. And those are the very things that leap to the fore-front of your mind when contemplating a self-improvement routine. Keeping your figure would be a cinch for you, if you could only eat.

4. The veranda/garden.

The veranda and garden are linked with the relaxation and re-freshment of the soul—places to take a break and unwind. If you wanted to see more of the garden, it's likely that you feel you're un-der constant pressure and stress—stress that can lead to missed workouts, poor eating habits, exhaustion, and lack of motivation. The first step you take toward improving your body may have to be relieving what's on your mind.

JUST THE RIGHT FIT

An alien entity or maleficent elf sneaks into your closet and drawers at night and, while you slumber, shrinks each article of your clothing by the slightest imperceptible amount. Only after weeks of these nightly visitations do you begin to notice the insidious effects. Pants that once fit comfortably now seem to pinch and confine, zippers and buttons refuse to close, and you have reached the final hole in your favorite belt. Yes, you must be the victim of some sinister clothes-shrinking demon. The only alternative is . . . unthinkable.

All jesting aside, much of the modern world has fallen out of shape. You can try to count calories or cut down on between-meals snacks, but study after study has shown there's only one proven and effective way to win the battle of the bulge: exercise. But exercise doesn't have to be a chore. Fitness centers and gyms have evolved ways to minimize the drudgery while maximizing results, and those who exercise regularly will tell you that a good workout can make you feel great. Believe it or not, there are even those who claim that exercise can be fun.

1. Some time ago, you became a member of a fitness club. But for some reason you stopped going. What was the reason you quit the club?

2. After an extended sojourn in the land of the couch potato, you decide to give routine exercise another try, this time at a different gym. Describe how you set about looking for a new place to work out.

3. While shopping around for a fitness center, you sign up for a free one-day trial session. Describe the appearance of the trial workout instructor.

4. You find a club that's to your liking and embark on a regimen of regular exercise. One day you notice that the gym always seems to be playing the same type of music in the background. What kind of music is it?

KEY TO "JUST THE RIGHT FIT"

I t has been said that sex is one of the best workouts you can give your body. Scientific evidence for that assertion remains scant, but when you get right down to it, who really cares? There are psychological links between physical exercise and physical love as well. Your responses to questions about the search for a good workout were determined in part by the way you go about selecting a sex partner.

1. The reason you gave for giving up on your gym is related to the reason you would lose interest in a lover.

"There was no variety, always just hammering away at the same thing over and over again." An understandable complaint, but there are, after all, certain anatomical limits to what the human body is capable of.

"Too fast paced and intense. I just couldn't keep up." You really do need to get into shape. But don't rush things—that leads only to pulled muscles, back strain, and burnout. There are beginner's courses designed especially for people like you.

"I was just too busy." You may be too busy at the moment, but that might also mean it's time to rethink your scheduling priorities. If you can't find thirty minutes for a quick workout a few days a week, you're probably working too hard.

"I'd exhausted all the possibilities at the facility. There were no challenges left for me there." Gulp. Maybe you should get a job as an instructor.

2. Your search for a new fitness club mirrors the way you go about finding a new partner.

"I'd gather information about as many different places as I could, review the pros and cons of each, and then make an informed decision." Effective? Probably. Romantic? No.

"I'd look for a place that was cheap and easy to get to." That's one way of deciding. But it might not be a good idea to tell them that if they ask how you found them.

"I'd ask a friend to recommend a good one." But what are you going to do if you bump into each other just as you're heading in for a workout?

3. Your description of the exercise trainer putting you through your one-day trial workout reflects the type of person you secretly would like to have a one-night stand with. It's probably safe to say you got someone who looks good in a leotard or spandex bike shorts. But what about those of you who described someone of the same sex? Don't feel too concerned; it's only for one workout. If you don't like it, you're under no obligation to sign up for a lifetime membership.

4. The background music you imagined is the kind of music you would prefer to listen to while having sex. If you aren't listening to it already, you might want to give it a try. Sometimes the right song can give you that little boost you need when you're trying to max out to a new personal best.

A Shoulder to Cry On

F or a young child, the first trip to summer camp can be exciting, but it can also be a very frightening experience. The first day, everyone else seems to know what they're doing, to belong to a circle of friends, and to have decided already which bunk they're going to sleep in. But with the help of the counselors and a few newfound friends, most kids seem to make it through that adjustment period without suffering any permanent damage, and it isn't unusual for a child who screamed, "I wanna go home!" on day one to cry, "I never wanna leave!" when the summer finally ends.

Imagine you're a counselor at a summer camp. A young first-timer knocks on your cabin door one night after lights-out and, with tears in his eyes, tells you he wants to go home. What do you say to the child?

KEY TO "A SHOULDER TO CRY ON"

I t's always easier to face sadness, fear, or loneliness when there's someone there to comfort you and say the things you need to hear. But not everyone responds to a cry for help in the same way. It takes a sensitive person to know just the right words to say to another who is feeling down. It almost requires getting inside that other person's mind and feeling their feelings with them. The words you spoke to the frightened child are actually the things you most want to hear when you yourself are troubled.

All some people need is simple reassurance: "Don't worry. Things will look better in the morning. I'll keep an eye out on you and everything will be fine."

Others just want to be told it's all right to cry: "That's right, just let it all out."

Others hate to be pitied: "Look at you crying like a baby. You think no one else is lonely? Grow up and get back to bed."

Whatever your response, finding the person who will say those things that help you overcome your darkest hours will be key to your happiness in life.

At the Water's Edge

T he winding river is both a source and a symbol of life. Rivers provide fresh water, transportation, and places to bathe, swim, fish, and relax outdoors, and as a result people have chosen to build their homes near rivers from time immemorial. Of course, there is always the danger of flooding, and the shallows serve as breeding grounds for parasites and hiding places for predators. But humans seem to have found that the benefits associated with natural waterways outweigh the risks, and few riversides today remain unsettled by our kind.

Imagine living in a home located near a river or stream. Which of the following best describes the property?

1. A home on a small island in the middle of a river.
2. A wide stream flowing past the home with a narrow footbridge across it.
3. A babbling brook running through one corner of the property.
4. A home whose property is crisscrossed by a maze of winding streams.

KEY TO "AT THE WATER'S EDGE"

(W) hile rivers may provide access to long-distance transportation by boat, on a personal scale they also frequently serve as impassable physical barriers. The relationship you saw between your home and the water nearby reflects your desire for social distance and personal space.

1. A home on a small island in the middle of a river.

You don't ask for infinite room to roam, just a quiet place to call your own—a place where you can be alone with your thoughts and escape from the pressures of society. If the home is a castle, you'd prefer yours to come with a moat.

2. A wide stream flowing past the home with a narrow footbridge across it.

You keep an intimate circle of personal relations, while holding the rest of the world at arm's length. That may make you a little harder to get close to than others, but it also means that when you call someone your friend, you always mean it.

3. A babbling brook running through one corner of the property.

You don't make a clear distinction between your social and private lives. You maintain an open door policy to the world and think of strangers as friends you just haven't met yet. That openness and spirit of hospitality ensures that come what may in life, you will never have to face it alone.

4. A home whose property is crisscrossed by a maze of winding streams.

You live in the midst of a labyrinthine social network, and you're preoccupied with the complex relationships between yourself and the people in your life. At times you may feel the outside world is always on the verge of flooding its banks, but that same maze of meandering channels also protects you from having any of those myriad streams rush straight in through your front door.

SIMULACRUMMY

I t may seem difficult to believe, but the cloning of mice, sheep, and monkeys is already old news, and the science of genetic engineering continues to forge ahead into never-before-explored territories where the lines between life and chemistry, progress and ethics, become blurred. What was once conceivable only as a plot for a low-budget science-fiction movie has recently become the everyday business of some high-budget biotech companies. And despite lingering doubts and protests, the day when humans are cloned seems to be approaching fast.

You are a scientist working on an experimental process to clone human beings. You have finally succeeded in cloning yourself, and using growth-acceleration technologies (patent pending), you are now the proud creator of an exact replica of your body, right down to the fingerprints. But although your clone is physically indistinguishable from you, it has a flaw in its personality that you do not find in your own. What is your clone's shortcoming or fault?

KEY TO "SIMULACRUMMY"

B y assuming the role of a research scientist, you afforded yourself the chance to inspect your character with the clear, cold eye of scientific objectivity. There are hidden flaws and unexpressed inclinations in our personalities that we studiously avoid noticing or thinking much about, but which refuse to remain entirely out of sight. The idea of a clone provides a screen upon which you can project your own submerged faults and repressed desires in safety. And in seeing them from a third-person perspective, you may begin to realize that they are not buried as deeply as you might have believed.

THE BOOK OF LIFE

T here's a book out there you've been searching for, but even you yourself don't know what it is. No subject, title, or author. No Dewey decimal or ISBN. Just a sense of certainty that when you find it, things will fall into place, and one of your life's great purposes will be fulfilled. Maybe you'll find it in a library or see it listed in an e-mail ad from an online store. You might stumble across a worn copy in the bargain bin in a used-book seller's basement. Or maybe you'll never find it at all. But one thing is certain: That book is out there somewhere. You just know it.

You are idly browsing the stacks of a large bookstore—not looking for any book in particular, just looking. You wander down one aisle and begin to search intently through a tall case of books. What is your impression of the books? When answering, describe your general impression of the books' content rather than naming specific authors, genres, or subject matter.

KEY TO "THE BOOK OF LIFE"

R eading can be a pleasurable activity, but no matter how much we may enjoy it, it still requires a certain amount of work. You may be able to leave a stereo or television playing in the background and get on with other things, but reading is an all-or-nothing affair. The working world requires a similar commitment of your time and effort, and the terms you used to describe the books that attracted you as you shopped mirror the things that you seek from your job.

Did you find yourself engrossed in a heartwarming love story or chuckling over a few well-turned jokes? That sounds like a great career; now, if only you can get someone to pay you to do it. Or did you perceive the books as a stimulating intellectual challenge? You're an employer's dream come true, but you run a very real risk of waking up one day and discovering that the only thing in your life is your job.

If the description you gave fits your current work environment, then it is likely that you feel satisfied in your present job. But if the description is the exact opposite of what your job is like, then maybe you need to spend less time browsing through bookstores and more time browsing the "Careers" section of the Sunday newspaper.

Trauma Central

T he emergency ward of a busy hospital is a chaos of wailing babies, patients moaning or struggling to describe their symptoms, and a disorderly procession of doctors, nurses, and paramedics all trying to do their job and stay out of each other's way. It is not an ideal environment for anyone involved, but in life-or-death situations people do whatever it takes to ensure survival. Perhaps the best that can be said for emergency rooms is that they are never boring, and TV producers have learned to bank on the voyeuristic thrill afforded by watching how average people respond in a health crisis.

Imagine yourself in the waiting room of the emergency center at a large hospital. As you wait, you begin to look at the faces of the people around you and recognize several acquaintances of yours among the patients. Match a person in your life with each of the following trauma cases:

1. Head swathed in gauze.
2. Face heavily bandaged.
3. Leg in a cast.

KEY TO "TRAUMA CENTRAL"

(T) he symptoms you associated with various people in your life show what you perceive as weaknesses in those people's characters.

1. Head swathed in gauze.

The head is a symbol of leadership and the ability to take command of a situation. The person you named as having a head injury is someone you feel you cannot trust or follow.

2. Face heavily bandaged.

The face represents the personality itself, and a person you imagined as facially disfigured is someone whose personality you have difficulty accepting or someone you just can't get along with.

3. Leg in a cast.

Legs represent stability and forward movement. The person you saw with a leg in a cast is someone you see as slowing you down or holding you back, either through sluggishness or simple clumsiness.

Did you feel some of these diagnoses of yours were a bit severe? Or maybe it's just uncomfortable to have the truth out in the open. But as all doctors know, the only way patients have a chance of getting better is by recognizing that they are sick.

THE WHEEL OF FORTUNE

C asinos make it their business to have something for everyone. If you can't stand blackjack, you might just love the slot machines. If the slots do nothing for you, you can take in a floor show. If the show is no good, you can always enjoy a cocktail on the house and just soak in the colorful atmosphere. The room is alive with flashing lights, jangling bells, and the palpable smell of money, and sometimes it seems difficult to form a rational thought with all the distractions the senses are offered.

Finally you succumb to the lure of the roulette wheel and the prospect of doubling your fortune in a single spin. You bet everything you have on red. The wheel spins. The ball skitters down. You close your eyes and hold your breath, thinking, Red. Red. Red. Come up red. The croupier cries, "Thirty-one, black!" and you turn and walk away without looking back.

What is your reaction on losing everything to this unkind twist of fate?

KEY TO "THE WHEEL OF FORTUNE"

(L) as Vegas is famous for two things: gambling and marriage. Both hold forth the promise of a lifetime of happiness to those who are fortunate in their decisions. But there's another side to that glinting coin, a side we don't like to think about much, and it promises only bitter disappointment and shattered dreams. The way that you felt about losing all your money is the way you would feel about a marriage that ended in divorce.

"How could I be so stupid? I'm never going to do that again!" How many times have we heard that before? Should we say "Good-bye" or "See you next time"?

"I guess this just wasn't my lucky day." Don't let it get you down. Even the best hit a slump from time to time.

"Well, I must've used up all my bad luck in one shot. Next time I'm sure to hit the jackpot." That's the spirit. Keep it up, and they're going to name a street after you in Atlantic City.

WHEN YOUR TASTES HAVE GROWN UP

Coffee may be the quintessential adult drink. That rich aroma, that slightly bitter edge, that feeling of warmth and mellow anticipation as you blow the steam away before taking your first sip. It's an experience you learn to enjoy as you leave childhood behind and serves as a sign that you have entered the grown-up world. Somehow, despite the caffeine, in the proper setting coffee soothes the nerves and relaxes the mind. A seat in a secluded corner of a coffee shop with a good book and some jazz playing softly in the background provides an ideal environment for many to take a step back from the stresses and strains of work, study, or life itself and enjoy the true luxury of doing nothing at all, if only for the time it takes to finish a cup.

You work hard enough. Take a moment now for yourself and enjoy one of the privileges of adulthood. Will it be French roast? Rich Colombian? A decadent mochaccino? Go ahead—indulge yourself. You've earned it.

1. It's that rarest of occasions, a day with nothing on the schedule, and you decide to enjoy some quality time with yourself in a coffee shop. Describe the atmosphere and ambience of the shop you choose.

2. You order a cup of coffee. What do you do while you're waiting for it to be brought to your table?

3. When the waiter delivers the coffee you ordered, how does it taste, and how is its temperature?

KEY TO "WHEN YOUR TASTES HAVE GROWN UP"

(C) offee in general and coffee shops in particular are closely linked with ideas of the adult world and social relations. Your responses to the questions in this scenario tell us something about the ways you perceive and manage stress in your own adult relationships.

1. The atmosphere you described is actually what you seek most in your workplace (or school). Some thrive in a lively environment elbow to elbow with other like-minded people. Others value quiet and solitude. Then there are those who don't care what the atmosphere is like, as long as the coffee comes in a bottomless cup.

2. The thing you did while waiting is related to a major source of stress or concern in your life.

Did you just sit and watch the other customers? You're a little too nervous about what others are doing, saying, and thinking. Just be yourself. Everyone else is.

Did you pull out a magazine and start reading, or look at the menu? You may need to get your nose out of the books and try a little more physical activity.

Did you sit and wait without doing anything at all? It's a sign you crave more stimulation from life and are looking for something to occupy your time.

3. How did the coffee taste? The flavor and temperature you imagined corresponds with the level of stress that you needlessly create for yourself. The better your experience of the coffee, the less stress you add to your life. If you imagined it was lukewarm, weak, too bitter, or scalding hot, you make problems where there are none to begin with. In your dreams, you can have anything you imagine—why not at least treat yourself to a nice cup of coffee?

RETURNS POLICY

I t can be hard to tell others how you really feel about them. Searching for just the right word or gesture to express your true feelings is never easy, and maybe it's never more difficult than when the person you're trying to address is someone you secretly love. For some, speaking those three little words "I love you" takes more courage than facing the gravest physical threat.

You have decided to admit your true feelings to a person you've loved from a distance for what seems like ages. You have brought a small gift to help show your sincerity and the depth of your love, but when you finally take that leap and offer yourself, that person says, "I'm sorry, but I can't take this from you. I'm in love with someone else."

Oof. Only time will heal your broken heart. The more immediate question is, What do you do with that unwanted gift?

1. Use it yourself.
2. Give it to someone else.
3. Throw it away.
4. Send it by mail to the person who turned it down.

KEY TO "RETURNS POLICY"

(F) ew experiences evoke as strong a reaction as the rejection of love. In extreme cases it can transform a simple passionate longing into a passionate longing for revenge. What you did with the rejected symbol of your love shows the degree to which you are able to recover and get on with your life or tend to linger in a world of broken dreams. This coincides with the levels of acceptance and persistence that you show in dealing with life's setbacks.

1. Use it yourself.

A stoic, you face reality head-on, and like a stoic, you prefer to keep a reminder of your heartache until it fades with the passage of time. You can be honest with yourself in saying, "That hurt," because you know you have the strength to take the pain and wear it like a badge of honor. But what you see as a demonstration of character can also be read as a way of taking revenge by never letting the other person forget how much he or she hurt you.

2. Give it to someone else.

You try to make the most of a bad situation by ridding yourself of an unpleasant reminder and simultaneously making another person happy. You don't put all your eggs in a single basket, and that gives you the freedom to forget about setbacks quickly and get on with life. And even though things may not have worked out to your liking this time, there is bound to be someone out there who will fall in love with the fundamental goodness of your nature.

3. Throw it away.

You may think that by throwing away the gift, you're throwing away all the memories and pain associated with it as well. But you are actually the type who dwells most deeply on hurts and rejections, unable to let go of the past. You may toss that ring in the river only to have it come out of your faucet the next morning. You can't throw away memories or pain, only learn to live with them.

4. Send it by mail to the person who turned it down.

You seek closure for yourself, even if it means ignoring the wishes of a person you thought you loved. This approach may actually be the healthiest for you because it lets you say, "I did everything that I set out to do. The rest was beyond my control."

LOOK OUT BELOW!

K eeping plants offers us the chance to give without any promise of reciprocation, gratitude, or reward. It's true that they ask for little—just some water and sunlight—but in a material sense they give even less in return. Nonetheless, house-plants enjoy a popularity that seems out of proportion to any decorative function they might perform. Perhaps we keep them because they fill a very human need: the need to be needed.

A potted plant you've been keeping on your balcony falls over the ledge it was sitting on. You run outside to survey the damage. What do you see?

1. The plant landed on the ground upright and intact.
2. The pot broke, but the plant seems to have survived the fall.
3. The pot and plant are both smashed beyond recovery.
4. For some strange reason, there is no sign of either plant or pot.

KEY TO "LOOK OUT BELOW!"

(T) he sheltered life of a potted plant corresponds to a hidden, guarded side of your character and the ways you try to keep the world from penetrating your social mask.

1. The plant landed on the ground upright and intact.

You appear to be strong and confident and are always eager to demonstrate your coolness under fire. But beneath that tough facade is a person more concerned with keeping up an image than actually living it.

2. The pot broke, but the plant seems to have survived the fall.

You seem calm and unflappable to others, but the reality is you just hate to show your emotions. Those pent-up feelings within you just keep growing and growing, and no pot can hold them in forever.

3. The pot and plant are both smashed beyond recovery.

You seem to be soft-spoken and self-effacing, but that "natural listener" is crying out for a chance to shine center stage. You are only waiting for an opportunity to break out of the self-imposed mold that confines you.

4. For some strange reason, there is no sign of either plant or pot.

   You excel at generating excitement and making others laugh, and people see you as the life of the party (even when there's no party in town). But that glib exterior hides a seriousness and even a shy side that you choose not to show the rest of the world.

FORE!

G olf is not something you can try on the spur of the moment; getting started in the sport is a major decision. It takes practice, patience, and preparation. You need the clubs, the shoes, the funny clothes, and of course the people to play with. Sometimes just getting to the point where you can finally tee off seems like more trouble than it's worth. But many first-timers find, as they settle into their stance with the sun on their backs and get set to address the ball, that all that work and waiting seem justified.

You are a novice trying your first full round of golf. You've hooked, sliced, hacked, whacked, and mulliganed your way through so far. It hasn't been pretty, but with some determination and after a little timely encouragement from your partner, you finally manage to sink the ball in the eighteenth hole. How do you feel now that you've completed the course?

KEY TO "FORE!"

S) ports, which combine physical exertion and physical pleasure, are psychologically associated with sex. The way you
felt on completing your first day of golf echoes the way you felt after your first sexual encounter.

"Hey, that was actually pretty fun. I guess it really isn't just for old
men." Now you're starting to get the picture. You probably thought
those old-timers were doing it just for the exercise, didn't you?

"That's it? I don't see what all the fuss is about. I've got better
things to do with my time." Like many of life's pleasures, golf is an
acquired taste. You might learn to enjoy it after a few more tries.

"I'm hooked. I'm definitely going to do this again next Sunday."
Why limit yourself? Some people even find the time to do it more
than once a week.

OODLES OF DOODLES

S choolchildren understand that page margins were made for doodling. It's almost sinful to let all that empty white space in a notebook go to waste. Scribbles, squiggles, googly-eyed faces, and hearts with arrows quickly grow and multiply, crowding into the writing space midpage. Give a child a notebook, a pencil, and sufficient time (say, the length of a history lesson on the Triangular Trade), and that boundless imagination spills forth onto page after page. We're taught that doodling is a bad habit, and the notebooks we keep as adults are neater (if duller) for it. But wouldn't it be a little sad to see a student whose notebooks were filled with page after page after page of neatly printed notes and flanked by clean margins on both sides?

Imagine you are a child, doodling happily away. You have begun to draw a picture of a bear. Which of the following looks most like your art?

1. A bear snoozing away contentedly.
2. A bear with its arms raised in a frightening pose.
3. A mother bear leading her cub.
4. A cute bear, like a stuffed toy.

KEY TO "OODLES OF DOODLES"

(I) n the psychology of animal imagery, the bear is a symbolic instance of the archetypal Great Mother. The characteristics of the Great Mother are as diverse as the different types of mothers. The aspect that you emphasized reflects your personal experience of motherly care. This experience plays a somewhat different role in the minds of women and men. For women, the bear you saw yourself drawing is your image of yourself as a mother or the kind of mother you expect to become; for men, it is the image you have of your own mother. Whether you are a man or a woman, this image may play an important part in your selection of a mate. They say that men end up marrying women who remind them of their moms, and women are drawn to men who bring out their maternal instincts.

1. Sleepy bear.

Your image of the mother is relaxed and easygoing, free to be herself and giving that same freedom to her children. She may not keep the neatest of dens, but her home is a place where you always feel welcome and safe to snuggle in for a long winter's nap.

2. Scary bear.

You see the mother as a powerful force, possibly even to the extent that she dominates the home. All mothers want what's best for their children; some demand it. Like it or not, in her family, this mother knows best.

3. Momma bear.

You have an idealized image of the mother: caring, loving, and tender. It may be stereotypical, but it's a nice stereotype to have. But try to have more reasonable expectations for real-world moms. After all, bears don't have to rush home from work in time to pick up the cubs from soccer practice and get dinner in the oven.

4. Cuddly bear.

Your image of the mother is someone who can't necessarily be relied upon, except to be lovable. As much as she may want to play Mommy, it seems that more often than not it's her own children who end up taking care of her. But as hopelessly adorable as she is, no one seems to mind.

TEN GRAND

en thousand dollars just isn't what it used to be. Twenty years ago, it could have bought you a new car. Fifty years ago, it could have bought you a house. Nowadays, it might get you a nice ten days in Hawaii for two or a remodeled kitchen. Still, the prospect of an extra ten grand is nothing to sneeze at.

Imagine you have won $10,000 in a random sweepstakes drawing. What do you do with the money?

1. Save it until you think of something you really want.
2. Surf that wave of good luck right down to the racetrack and put the whole $10,000 down on a horse.
3. Blow it all on an extravagant party to celebrate your good fortune.
4. Take that romantic trip abroad you've always dreamed of.

KEY TO "TEN GRAND"

(W)inning a sweepstakes is like suddenly falling for someone—you can't make these kinds of things happen, they
just happen to you out of the blue. But true love is something
earned. Unlike infatuation or simple physical lust, it demands hard
work and dedication. The way you reacted to your sudden good
fortune shows your worst habits in love.

1. Save it until you think of something you really want.

You seem to be cautious and serious, but it's because you're
always looking out for number one. You don't let yourself get
caught up in too much feeling for others, and your partners may
end up feeling that you are always on the lookout for something
better. The best investment you can make in a relationship is in-
vesting yourself.

2. Surf that wave of good luck right down to the racetrack and put
the whole $10,000 down on a horse.

They say you can't have too much of a good thing, and you
take that argument to its logical conclusion. "If one lover is good,
then two must be better, and three, four, ten, even better than that!
The sky's the limit!" I don't want to jinx you, but that lucky streak
of yours is bound to end sooner or later.

3. Blow it all on an extravagant party to celebrate your good fortune.

Money is made to be spent and love is made to be, well, made.
You don't waste precious energy weighing the costs and benefits or
comparison-shopping. But you need to consider saving a little
something for the future. A real love can last forever, but no party
can.

4. Take that romantic trip abroad you've always dreamed of.

You seek your pleasures in foreign places but also want the security of being able to return home when you're done. You feel that
your diverse experience has broadened you as an individual and
helps to sate your insatiable curiosity. But your habit of spending
too much time in exotic ports of call might just get you quaran-
tined by the domestic authorities when you finally make it home.
You want it both ways, but love requires you to put down permanent roots.

FROZEN IN TIME

I n fantasy, we can be all-powerful—invincible in conflict and irresistible in love—an omnipotent force in an imagined universe where even the laws of physics cease to apply. Imagine flying, moving mountains, traveling to the far side of the galaxy at faster than light speed. The mind can do these things without breaking a sweat. Our bodies are confined by limitations and laws on all sides, but in our imaginations, we can be free.

Imagine you have a single chance to freeze time and walk about the world as if it were a wax museum. You can do whatever you like. Just what is it you would like to do before the clock's hand thaws?

KEY TO "FROZEN IN TIME"

J ust as the body is bound by the laws of physics, behavior is itself ruled by social constraints. Freud called the part of the mind that monitors the self's unacceptable urges "the superego." The superego is most concerned with real behavior and operates much more weakly in the realm of fantasy. The things you saw yourself doing in a world where laws no longer apply to you show how powerful your own superego, or moral conscience, is. It's been said, "Character is what you do when you think no one else is looking." But the one gaze you can't avoid is your own.

If you merely took the chance to travel for free, snoop around some exciting forbidden location, or just play a good practical joke, it shows a consistency in your standards that speaks of normal moral character. But people who took the opportunity to commit more serious crimes such as stealing a large sum of money or doing harm to others have revealed that their behavior is ruled more by social laws than a strong internal standard.

If you decided that you would keep the world in permanent suspension, so that you could wander it freely forever, you might want to give that decision a little more thought. A frozen world is inevitably cold.

WHO'S GOT THE BUTTON?

H ow do you make your choices when shopping for clothes? Are you lured by certain colors or patterns? Do some brands have the power to make you reach for your credit card? Or are you an inveterate bargain hunter who can't resist the chance to save 40 percent, even if it's something you don't really want or need? Think of the clothes that are already in your closet. You may see patterns other than paisley, tartan, and flower print begin to emerge. Specifically, think of your favorite blouse or shirt. Now visualize the number of buttons on the front. How many buttons are there, and how do you keep them buttoned when you have the shirt on? (Choose the nearest answer from the choice below.)

1. It has more than five buttons down the front, and I button them all.

2. There are two or three buttons on the front, and I button them all.

3. There is a row of buttons on the shirt, and I leave one or two at the top unbuttoned.

4. There are no buttons on the shirt.

KEY TO "WHO'S GOT THE BUTTON?"

(F) ew people consciously make button count a deciding fac-
tor when choosing their wardrobes. But as in most matters
of taste, the subconscious plays an important role. There are many
things in life that are uncontrollable, but there are also some in
which we have the power of final say. Buttoning is one. Deciding
how we spend our money is another. Both behaviors are ways of expressing one's sense of freedom or control, and your buttoning
habits actually reflect the way you handle your finances.

1. It has more than five buttons down the front, and I button them all.
    You are very conscientious with your money, never splurging
or spending recklessly. Regardless of your income, you set a budget, follow it, and somehow manage to put something away as well.
Some might call you tight, but you're on the straight-and-narrow
path to financial security.

2. There are two or three buttons on the front, and I button them all.
    You take a middle-of-the-road approach in managing your
personal finances. You aren't afraid to spend on the things you
want, but you don't like to throw money away frivolously, either.
You are one of those rare people in control of, and not controlled
by, their money.

3. There is a row of buttons on the shirt, and I leave one or two at the top unbuttoned.

You have specific goals and invest every spare penny in them. On the other hand, you're a moderate spender in areas not directly related to realizing your dreams. That single-minded sense of purpose makes you a prime candidate for conversion one day to the buttoned-down look adopted by people who are used to getting what they want from the world.

4. There are no buttons on the shirt.

Your fiscal motto is "A penny saved is a penny wasted." You charge like a wounded bull, and don't look back to survey the damage. Get used to the jeans and T-shirt look. If you keep up the pace, that might be all you're able to afford.

KEEPING THE PEACE

Parks and playgrounds are intended to be places for quiet relaxation and childhood games, but they can be the stage for some less pleasant scenes as well. Kids will be kids, and sometimes that means bad little kids. The child's world is not all hopscotch and hide-and-seek—there are plenty of other ways to pass the time when teachers and parents aren't around.

Walking past a small playground one day, you see two young children engaged in a serious-looking fight. No other adults are around. How do you respond (if at all)?

KEY TO "KEEPING THE PEACE"

(A) fight between children is difficult to ignore—you know it's not really your business, but still, the urge to intervene is strong. Something about the situation seems to invite the voice of reason to speak out and set things right. The same could be said of illicit love affairs between adults. The way you responded to the fighting kids shows the way you might respond if you learned that a friend was having an adulterous affair.

Did you step in and try to break it up? ("Look at the two of you. You should know better!") Or did you just shrug it off and ignore it? ("Let them go at it. It's just part of the growing process.")

There's no one correct answer to the dilemma of whether to break it up or let it slide. But ask yourself, If it was my child, would I want someone to step in? Chances are good that most other people feel the same.

A FLASH OF RED

F rom red as a rose to red as a beet, when we see red it affects us emotionally. Scientific experiments have shown that people asked to remain in a room with red walls become more passionate, aggressive, and easily aroused than people in rooms with muted backgrounds. Research has even shown that exposure to red can make the body temperature rise. Red may be at the low end of the spectrum of light, but it has power to move us like no other color.

Imagine three women, each of whom is fond of the color red and uses it to accent her appearance. The first of these women has her nails painted red, the second wears red lipstick, and the third has her hair colored the same shade. Now imagine their personalities and describe each in detail.

KEY TO "A FLASH OF RED"

(A)lthough in some ways we all react similarly to the color red, there are also significant differences in our psychological responses. This is not simply a matter of taste or acculturation but seems to have roots that sink deeper into the mind. In the natural world, red is the universal sign of danger, a way for one animal to let potential foes and competitors know, "Careful, I bite and I'm poisonous." But this same shade is also powerfully seductive, and for animals attuned to the same sexual frequency, it can signal that the mating season has begun. In nature as in fashion, it's not the color itself; it's what you do with it.

The images you had of the three red-accented women reveal the kinds of women you view as friend and foe. This results in different interpretations, depending on whether the respondent is male or female.

Female respondents.

The woman with red nails is seen as a threat and represents the type of woman you can't imagine yourself ever getting along with. On the other hand, you feel a strange and compelling attraction to the woman with red lips. The woman with red hair is an image of the type of woman that you hope you will never become.

Male respondents.

The red-nailed woman is the kind of person you fear will use or make a fool of you, while the red-lipped woman is the type you can imagine yourself falling wildly in love with. The redheaded woman represents the type you can't see yourself being attracted to, no matter how physically beautiful she may be.

FUNNY BUSINESS

I t's easy to laugh at other people, but making others laugh is a different story. There are some people who will do anything to achieve that end, but few of us are willing to resort to making fools of ourselves for a chuckle. True comics have mastered the balancing act of tickling the funny bone without either inflicting pain or injuring their own dignity. A good sense of humor is a rare commodity and consistently rates as the attribute most people look for in their partners and friends. Shared laughter brings people together and leaves a bond rooted in the knowledge that someone else out there got the joke.

1. You are making your debut as a stand-up comedian. You want to be a hit, but there is one person you definitely don't want to show up to watch you perform. Who is that person?

2. What do you see as the single most important ingredient in determining success in the comedy business?

3. During your act, you made a single blunder. What kind of mistake was it, and how did you attempt to recover?

4. One member of the audience laughed harder and longer than anyone else. Who was this fan of yours?

KEY TO "FUNNY BUSINESS"

(L) aughter is rich in psychological associations of anxiety and escape, control and subversion, while the idea of a stage implies an audience, which also implies being watched and evaluated by others. Against this background, assuming the role of the comedian allows you to place yourself in the position of exposing your fears and weaknesses for the world to see.

1. Who was it that you didn't want to see your act? A lover? One of your parents? Your boss? You might think that you chose them because they were the butt of a number of your jokes, but actually that person is someone you wish never to disappoint or show weakness to. There are some people in life we just don't want to have laughing at us.

2. What did you name as the secret to success as a comic? The thing you saw as essential is something you feel you need more of to succeed in your own social relations. Perfect timing? High-energy performance? A good manager? Those things are important, but perhaps it all boils down to always knowing what people want to hear.

3. The mistake or flub you made mirrors a major blunder from your own past that you have always regretted. If you said you dropped the mike midact, you have probably had more than your share of clumsy accidents. Those who had no response for a heckler have

had bad experiences getting flustered under fire or when being criticized. If you said you offended the audience, it's likely you tend to blurt out the first thing that pops into your head without thinking about who may be standing within earshot.

Your attempted recovery represents the way you think will help you to avoid or minimize the effects of similar mistakes in the future. You can try to ignore it and get on with your routine, but sometimes the best recovery is just to admit your goof and laugh at yourself.

4. Joking is a psychologically complex phenomenon. In one sense, it involves having the power to control others through the ability to make them laugh. But that power can be exercised only by acknowledging and catering to the other's sense of what is funny and involves assuming a risk of failure in the attempt to please. The person you named as your biggest fan is someone you do not want to have power over you. This may be out of a sense of friendly rivalry or rooted in more intense competition, but that person also holds a key to your own growth as an individual by providing you with the stimulus you need to polish your act.

SEEKING APPLICANTS

Looking for your first job after graduation is a stressful process. It means hours spent working through your interviewing strategy, checking and rechecking your résumé, even rehearsing your posture and smile in front of the mirror. It's all about making a good impression; about letting them know you've got what they need. You're out there competing with a hundred other grads with the same GPA, the same part-time job experience, and the same extracurricular interests. A new suit and haircut aren't enough to set you apart from the crowd—you need to find a way to make the people in HR see the real you.

1. You have landed an interview at the company of your first choice. On the day of your interview, you are called down to a meeting room and you see that you're going to be interviewed by a team. What is the average age of the people on the panel of interviewers?

2. The interview is rigorous and thorough, with questions ranging from the simple "getting to know you" variety to ones that were clearly intended to rattle your cage. You manage to field every question thrown at you, but one in particular leaves a strong impression. What is that question?

3. Just when you are beginning to relax and feel the job is in the bag, one of the interviewers begins to point out your shortcomings

and weak points. What characteristics does your critic list among your faults?

4. That night, the phone rings. It's the HR manager calling with an offer! What do you say in response?

KEY TO "SEEKING APPLICANTS"

(C) ongratulations—you did it! Landing a job is cause for celebration, but it also means taking on a host of new responsibilities and challenges. It's one of the most important decisions you can make in determining the course of your life, almost like committing yourself to another person. In fact, there are many parallels between work and relationships; there are assignments of expectations and accountability, a need for teamwork and occasional sacrifice, and far-reaching consequences for success and failure. It's no wonder, then, that your responses to this scenario also reveal some of your hopes and expectations regarding romance and love.

1. The average age of your interviewers is the age of the person you see as your ideal partner. An interview is an opportunity not just to make, but also to form, an impression. The age of the imaginary decision makers at your ideal employer reflects your own preferences in the age of people you want to be involved with. A great majority of people see their ideal partner as roughly the same age or slightly older. If you said the panel comprised people much older than you, it may be that you have an eye for the "silver foxes."

2. The question that sticks most in your mind is actually something you would secretly like to ask your lover or spouse.

"Why did you choose this company?" We've all wanted to ask, "Why did you pick me?"

"Tell us about your hobbies and interests." Translation: "What do you do when I'm not around?"

"What makes you so interested in trying out this position?" That's a loaded question, but sometimes one that needs to be asked.

3. The faults that your interviewer listed are actually things your partner loves you for. A flaw that you acknowledge loses much of its negative force, and there's no shortcoming that can't be turned into a strength. The things that you have seen are wrong with you are things that you have already taken steps to compensate for.

"You're overconfident." That self-assuredness lends strength to others.

"Not proactive enough." You're easygoing, easy to live with, and easy to love.

"Too inexperienced." You bring a sense of freshness and boundless potential to a relationship.

4. Your reply to the offer of employment shows how you would react to a marriage proposal.

"Really? Are you serious! Great! I can't wait to get started." That's sure to start things off on the right foot, but you may want to play it a little closer to the vest until the deal is sealed. Too often people mistake eagerness for desperation.

"I'd like to think it over for a few days." That seems to be a sensible approach. There's no reason to jump in headfirst. After all, this is a very big commitment.

"Well, I've had a few other offers as well, so I'm going to take some time to weigh my options." Careful now, don't get too sure of yourself—it's likely they've had other applicants, too.

DREAM HOME

S ome people see their home merely as a shelter from the elements or a place to crash after a long day spent outside. But most attach deeper significance to the place they call home—feelings of safety, comfort, warmth, and love. However one may feel, the image of the home is defined by experiences and memories and gives shape to your dream of a perfect place to be. We've all had the experience of visiting someone's home for the first time and thinking, This is exactly how I imagined it would be. Homes are for hearts as well as bodies, and they tend to take on the characters of their occupants over time.

How would you describe your ideal home, the home you see yourself most comfortable in? Let's open the door and take a peek inside.

1. After years of hard work and saving, you are considering the purchase of your dream home. When you open the front door to begin the tour, there is a staircase immediately before you. Is it brightly illuminated or dimly lit?

2. The house has not been used for some time. Hallway, toilet, bathtub, dining room—which is most badly in need of cleaning? Which is the best kept?

3. As you walk from room to room, you notice the front door is still slightly open, and someone is peeping in through the crack. Who is that person?

KEY TO "DREAM HOME"

(A) ttaining your ideal home represents the fulfillment of your worldly aspirations and dreams in life. The image you had of your tour through your dream home is tied to your image of what the future holds in store for you.

1. The staircase symbolizes what lies ahead. Those who pictured a well-lit staircase have a clear set of goals and expectations for what is to come. Those who imagined a dark stairway have difficulty conceiving the direction their lives will take.

2. The area you perceived as dirtiest reveals an area in your life that you believe will give you the most problems in the future, while the cleanest area is what you hope will be the key to your happiness and success.

Hallway. A dirty hallway is a sign of anxiety about difficulties relating to other people, while a clean hallway signifies the hope of an unobstructed course through the world of interpersonal relationships.

Toilet. Those who imagined a clean toilet attach the most importance to financial security and success, while those who saw a dirty toilet fear money problems, debt, and bankruptcy in the future.

Bathtub. The bath is a symbol of health, and its level of cleanliness reflects one's hopes or concerns about physical well-being and sickness. A dirty tub equates with a fear of future illness and debilitation; a clean tub shows an attachment of great importance to the maintenance of good health.

Dining room. The dining room is the space devoted to the family as a whole. A dirty dining room is an omen of familial strife to come, while a clean dining room shows that the family is that person's highest priority.

3. Doors protect the home from the world outside. By peering through the door to watch as you visited your dream home, the person you named breached an important line of defense. That intruder is someone you perceive as a potential threat to your future happiness. It may even be someone you could never imagine intentionally causing you harm. It may be that person makes you uneasy because the people we love have the greatest power to hurt us. But then, the unconscious also has ways of sensing danger that the conscious mind chooses to ignore.